14^{95}

A Collector's Guide To
PERSONAL
COMPUTERS
And Pocket Calculators

by

Dr. Thomas F. Haddock

ISBN 0-89689-098-8

BOOKS AMERICANA
INC.

TABLE OF CONTENTS

Introductory Comments

This history of the personal computer has been treated many times, in magazine articles, audio-visual works, individual chapters of computer-history books, and in books devoted specifically to the subject. The motivating forces of the evolution of the personal computer, as well as how the early market responded, have been well documented. However, there as yet has been no in-depth examination of the individual machines that were the object of this history. This book reviews the developmental history of the personal computer, but only to provide a general context for the main body of work: a chronological listing of over 600 personal computers and calculators, reaching back to their earliest years. Containing over 300 illustrations, this is the first work to portray the developmental history of the personal computer in a detailed and specific way.

In addition to chronicling evolutionary history, this catalog is the first collector's guide to personal computers and calculators. As such, collector values are given for each machine. In many cases a discussion of the historical significance of a machine, and other factors influencing its collectibility, are given. This new approach to treating personal computers and calculators reflects their emerging status as historical and collector's items.

ACKNOWLEDGEMENTS:

A book such as this could not have been completed without the help of many people. I would like to thank the many historians and archivists at the numerous companies who were contacted during the writing of this book, the numerous Hobbyists who discussed their early machines and allowed them to be photographed, and Kirstin Fredrickson, who helped in the preliminary gathering of information.

TRADEMARKS:

I-1. A BRIEF HISTORY OF MICROCOMPUTERS

The origins of the personal computer can be traced to the mid-1950s in the form of various battery-powered, toy-like kits that sold in the price range below $20. With names like Geniac and Brainac, they were born out of the fascination with the only computers existing at the time, mainframes with names like ENIAC, EDSAC, BINAC, and, of course, the UNIVAC whose name was almost synonymous with the word computer at the time. These kit machines were comprised of rotating fiberboard disks with bolts acting as contacts and series of flashlight bulbs as output. They could perform only a few simple tasks, such as converting binary numbers to hexadecimal, but were the closest thing to a digital electronic computer commercially available to hobbyists.

Aside from these early and rather obscure pioneers, the personal computer market essentially lay dormant until the early 1970s when the creation of the first microprocessor chip, Intel's 4-bit 4004 introduced in 1971, made inexpensive personal computers possible. The Scelbi-8H, introduced in 1973 and based on the Intel 8008, was typical of the first personal computers in that it was a product for the enthusiast/hobbyist only. The first commercially-offered microcomputer-based digital electronic personal computer was the Mark 8, a kit machine offered through mail order by its designer, Jonathon Titus. Introduced in a hobbyist-oriented article in the July 1974 *Radio-Electronics* (which told about the new machine and how to order the kit), it cost about $50, but required several hundred dollars worth of additional parts to build. These early machines had little usefulness, but mainly served to introduce hobbyists to the microprocessor.

These early microcomputers went largely unnoticed. The machine that truly launched the personal computer market was the Altair 8800. Introduced in 1975, it was based on the successor to the 8008, the Intel 8080, and was available as a kit or in assembled form for $395 and $650 respectively. It was offered by a small electronics company, MITS, and was the product of its owner, Edward Roberts. Like the Mark 8, the Altair 8800 was introduced in an electronics hobbyist magazine. The January 1975 issue of *Popular Electronics* billed the new machine as a "kit to rival the commerical models," referring to the minicomputers available at the time. The tremendous commerical success of the Altair 8800 founded the personal computer market. It defined the S-100 bus (initially called the "Altair Bus") and spawned clone manufacturers and manufacturers of add-on boards and other components. Companies such as IMSAI, SWTPC, Cromemco, and Processor Technology quickly sprang up in its wake. Purchasers of computers needed printers, tape or disk drive, and other peripherals to effectively use their machines, and suppliers such as Shugart, OAE, and others began to satisfy this demand.

For the most part, these early machines were aimed at the home user and hobbyist rather than the serious business user, and significant knowledge was required to configure them as practical machines. Input was typically through rows of toggle switches, with displays comprised of lines of LEDs that could only display a single binary number at a time. While more convenient I/Os could, and often were, adapted to these machines, they still remained difficult to interact with. This, along with the extensive knowledge required to build and operate them, limited their market to dedicated enthusiasts.

Instead of a single motherboard with the microprocessor integrated onto it, as in today's machines, these early machines typically had a backplane bus. Referred to at the time as the "mainframe," this bus was populated with individual cards, including one containing the microprocessor. This gave a very flexible system which allowed the hobbyist to easily alter or improve input, output, display and other functions, and even to change the type of microprocessor. Virtually all of these early machines offered merely a starting place for the hobbyist, and were "customized" to operate as the kit builders saw fit. This versatility poses a problem today for the collector in that a "standard" configuration is difficult to determine.

In 1977 the Apple II, Radio-Shack TRS-80, and Commodore PET were introduced. These machines were offered in relatively standard configurations, and each was a completely assembled machine with an integral keyboard. The Commodore had an integral CRT monitor, and the TRS-80 and Apple had the circuitry to drive a monitor built in. They all came with BASIC in ROM, and thus could do useful work for a relatively inexperienced purchaser minutes after being unpacked. The extensive collection of software that was quickly available for these machines included games, word processors, and spreadsheets, and made them enjoyable and useful to a wider segment of the population, extending far beyond electronics hobbyists and experts. They found immediate use in the business world. Sales of these machines grew rapidly, and the era of the "appliance computer" began.

By 1981 the personal computer market was thriving. Numerous software programs of all sorts were available for the various machines on the market, many of which ran the CP/M operating system. On August 12, 1981, based on this growing market, IBM introduced the 5150 PC. With a base price of about $1600, it was available with up to 64 K of RAM and either cassette or 5.25-inch floppy disk drive storage. It was the first offering from this established mainframe computer manufacturer, and with IBM's strong reputation behind it, it sold rapidly. In one stroke it established a new hardware and software standard. MicroSoft's disk operating system, known as MS-DOS or PC-DOS, was supplied with these machines and became the standard for microcomputers. As with previous advances in the market, clone, accessory, and software industries sprang up around the new standards as the personal computer market moved into the "DOS" stage. Many of the old manufacturers either adapted or went out of business. However, many of those marketing in the mainstream enjoyed the rapid growth of the personal computer market into the form it has today.

By 1984, with the 8088-based PC and its numerous clones well established, IBM introduced the PC AT (Advanced Technology). This machine ran at 6 MHz, had a 16-bit data bus, and used the Intel 80286 processor. It was well-received, and spawned another generation of clones. However, while the basic technology was improved, it represented an evolutionary rather than revolutionary change, and virtually all preexisting DOS software would run on the new AT-class machines.

The mainstream development of personal computers has continued this way up to the present date, with the introduction by Intel of the 80386 and 80486 microprocessors and the associated versions of DOS-based machines.

In 1987, IBM introduced the IBM PS/2 line, deviating from their previously-set standards of bus design. The new "micro channel" bus, while technologically superior to the previous bus, was incompatible with it. As before, some clone manufacturers followed IBM's lead. However, even IBM was unable to completely redirect the market, and clones of earlier versions of the PC, using updated versions of the old bus (now referred to as "Industry Standard Architecture" or ISA) and running updated versions of the original DOS operating system, continued to comprise a significant part of the personal computer market.

While the market clearly took direction from IBM and MicroSoft, other types of machines have remained in production. The Apple II, and its later variants, still sold well long after the introduction of the IBM PC. Commodore has also offered various types of machines. Graphic User Interface (GUI) machines evolved to widen the personal computer market to people who were intimidated by the command-line driven machines. The GUI machines operate through manipulating pictures, or icons, on the screen with pointers controlled by a "mouse" or other pointing devices. They require very little knowledge of computers to operate. Apple's LISA of 1982 was an early commercial offering, but the Apple Macintosh, introduced in 1984 was the first truly successful GUI machine, and established GUI as a legitimate and commercially viable product. Other interfaces evolved. Machines such as GRiD's GRiDPad introduced a convenient and portable alternate to the keyboard for input. A special pen could be used on its screen to input data.

One of the most significant trends in the personal computer market since the introduction of the IBM PC has been the evolution of portable computers. The concept has been around for some time. The BABY! of 1976 was contained in a suitcase but required the use of an external monitor, while the Bytemaster of 1978 was a completely integrated machine. However, the age of the portable computer began in earnest when Adam Osborne introduced the Osborne I portable in 1981. The size of a small suitcase, it had two 5.25-inch minifloppy drives, a 5-inch diagonal CRT, a keyboard (that made up the bottom of the case when stored), and even disk-storage compartments. Selling for $1795, including several pieces of software, it was an immediate success. The suitcase theme was continued in the newly-established IBM/DOS standard by the Compaq portable in 1982.

This product spawned the successful Compaq Computer Company, now a manufacturer of desktop as well as portable machines.

As miniaturization continued, suitcase-sized machines, the "Luggables," gave way to the "Laptops." Typical of the latter category was the Zenith SupersPort, weighing about twelve pounds with dimensions of about twelve inches square and three inches high. The next stage, the "notebook" computers, had a footprint about the size of a pad of paper. By 1989 Compaq was selling the LTE, a 7-pound, 8.5 by 11 by about two-inch thick machine with a 20 or 40 megabyte hard drive and a built-in modem. The smallest category of portables, the "handhelds" or "palmtops", had a hazy beginning in variants of the programmable calculators that appeared in the early to mid 1970s. However, by 1991 Hewlett-Packard was selling the HP 95LX, a fully IBM/DOS compatible computer only the size of a hand calculator with a QWERTY keyboard and 512 K of RAM. The handhelds have yet to share the same standard storage media as the larger machines (floppy and hard disks), and, by their very size, face problems with displays and keyboards. In other aspects they are completely comparable in method of operation and performance with the desktop machines of only a few years back.

Calculators differ from computers in that they perform a more limited and specific set of operations than computers. Small mechanical calculating devices have existed in many commercial forms long before electronic computers were first built. Perhaps the pinnacle of these devices were the beautiful Kurta hand calculators. Desktop digital electronic calculators, however, were introduced in 1963 when the British Bell Punch company produced the first commercial model. This was quickly followed by products from Texas Instruments and Hewlett-Packard, and these evolved into the hand calculator in the early 1970s.

I-2. A DESCRIPTION OF THIS WORK

The personal computer has taken many forms in the short time it has existed, ranging from inexpensive and virtually useless toys, to costly professionally-designed systems bordering on the expense and complexity of minicomputers. For a catalog such as this, a clear and simple definition is needed to determine which machines are eligible for inclusion. While there are many possible definitions as to what constitutes a personal computer, the following criteria has been used here:

1) The device must be manufactured for sale to the general public, at least in kit form. "Homebrew" or other custom machines are not included. Kits must contain at least one part that is incorporated in the finished machine. "Kits" comprised solely of instructions are not included.

2) The device must be aimed (at least in part) at the home or hobbyist market, as opposed to being marketed exclusively to the professional or scientific market.

3) The device must operate digitally.

4) The device must operate electrically or electronically (this distinction has significance in discussing the early toylike machines of the 1950s).

5) The device must have the capability of being programmed for different tasks by its operator (either by changing the hardware or software configuration).

In the interests of showing historical continuity, some close relatives of important machines (such as the IBM 5100, the IBM 3720, and the Xerox Alto) have been included in this listing in violation of requirement number 2.

For calculators, the same basic definition was used, although the requirement for programmability was dropped. This raises the problem of programmable calculators, which, by the above definition, would be computers. However, the evolutionary history of programmable calculators, their general physical layout and appearance (one-line displays, numeric keypads instead of QWERTY keyboards, etc.), and their general lack of convenient storage media, identify them more as calculators than computers. There is clearly a hazy borderline between programmable calculators and hand-held computers, and many categorizations in these two groups have been judgement calls. The programmable Hewlett-Packard 65 and Texas Instruments SR-52, with their magnetic-card storage might reasonably have been categorized as handheld computers, but their user numeric keypad interfaces, and close physical similarity to the hand-calculators they derived from, put them in the calculator category. While the Hewlett-Packard 95LX has the apparent evolution, appearance, size, and feel of the earlier Hewlett-Packard programmable calculators, its QWERTY keyboard, half-screen display, and its MS-DOS operating system put it in the computer category. Strictly fitting these definitions was, of course, not enough for a machine to be included in this compilation. In the case of Section II-1, covering the early hobbyist machines, virtually every machine discovered has been cataloged. All of the early pioneers are of historical significance to at least some degree. For the later machines the question of historical significance was more carefully considered. Inclusion of a machine does not mean that it represented a major step forward; some represented no technological change at all, or even retrograde motion. There are machines included merely because they were popular and well-known. However, this in itself represents historical significance.

Aside from the earliest group of machines, age was not a factor influencing selection. Examples of this are the Compaq LTE and the Hewlett-Packard 95LX, both modern machines. The LTE is of clear historical significance due to its pioneering the full-function notebook category of computers. It was a classic and a collector's item from the moment it was introduced, though it will not be generally recognized as such for some time. The only market value of the LTE is as a functional item; it has as yet no collector's value. Nonetheless, it is included here for its historical significance.

The values of such newer machines have a different basis than those of the earlier machines. Since they are determined principally by the machine's utility value, they fall with time. This is in contrast to the early machines whose values are determined by the collector's market, and typically rise with time.

The price ranges given in this guide are for machines in this condition:

-basic system essentially complete, as originally sold.

-case, keyboard, monitor, etc. showing some wear and a few noticeable scratches, but not excessively scuffed or scraped. No cracks.

-it is not assumed that the system operates.

Of course, the value of any individual machine depends on its condition, and can be higher or lower than the ranges given here. A full set of original boxes, manuals, and disks can increase price by as much as 100 percent if they are in good condition. Additional accessories such as floppy drives, monitors, etc. are listed separately in Chapter Three.

The prices given in this catalog are derived from information from sales of machines to collectors or users by knowledgeable sellers. Aside from some of the well-recognized and supported machines, such as the Apple II and IBM PC, most of the machines listed here are used only by a few dedicated users, and would typically be classed as obsolete and worthless electronics. While a few of the early machines, such as the Scelbis, Mark 8, Altairs, Apple I, and the Hewlett-Packard 35 and 45 calculators, are generally recognized as valuable collector's items, for the most part, they are regarded as worthless by non-collectors who no longer use them and have lost track of other users. Such machines are often available free, and collections have been made using acquisition at no cost as a criteria. This is often the case in areas of collecting where the objects are undergoing a transition from being regarded as old and worthless to being regarded as objects of historical value. Almost all genuine areas of collecting have gone through this transition. In the past thirty years cars, baseball cards, toys, and dolls have gone from items generally of interest only when they are new and useful, to valuable and avidly collected objects. In fact, many have even become the intense focus of investors whose only interest in them is that of financial return. At the present time, old personal computers and hand calculators are still regarded by many as junk. However, this is changing. The computer columnist, John C. Dvorak, has discussed collecting computers in both the January 12, 1988 and June 11, 1991 issues of *PC Magazine*. The number of collectors is growing, and a society of collectors, the Computer Collector's Register, was founded a few years ago. Hence the need for a guidebook.

It should be noted that while historical significance frequently indicates the desirability of a machine to collectors, it does not insure high price. Here, as elsewhere, price is fixed by supply and demand. While the historical significance of the Apple II is clear, the large number of these machines still available prevents them from attaining the price of the Altar 8800, another historically prominent machine available in much smaller quantities.

Since a focus of this work is the historical value of personal computers and hand calculators, the "standard" configuration for each machine, that is, the configuration in which it was typically advertised and sold, will be described when possible. Consideration of an object as an historical artifact changes the way it is appreciated and valued. Objects remaining at or close to their original configuration are generally considered to retain more historical "value" than those that have been modified and updated over time.

In many cases, especially in the early days, the personal computer as it was sold was merely a starting place for building up a system, and couldn't be practically used without supplying a keyboard, CRT, and paper-tape drive or cassette recorder. However, in most cases, the originally-offered configuration is the most desirable from an historical and collector's standpoint, and it will be specified here whenever possible.

It is also important to note the value of boxes, manuals, and associated materials that accompanied the objects when they were sold. These materials carry information about the object's place in history, and contribute to its historical and collectible value. In many cases, original packaging, manuals and disks, has as much value as the hardware itself. Software, being merely instructions and information rather than a physical object, is ethereal in nature, and its "packaging" has more collector's value than the code itself.

With the exception of software, the prices given in this guide assume the object is complete with all components originally delivered with it (although it may not be operable), but do not assume the presence of packaging, manuals, original software disks, etc. The presence of these items can in some cases increase the value of an object up to many times its listed value.

The main chapters of this guide are broken down by type of equipment. The sections within each chapter appear roughly in chronological order. While there is some temporal overlap between the sections, on the whole they can be taken as an outline of the development of the personal computer. Within each section equipment is listed in chronological order by its date of introduction. In some cases, these dates were difficult to determine, and position in the listing has been fixed by the earliest located evidence of production (as described in the "Production" heading).

While the classification of some machines are clear, the Altair clearly belongs in the "Hobbyist" grouping and the Apple II in the "Appliance" category, the classification of others is arguable. There are many judgement calls in a compilation such as this, and some devices placed in one section might legitimately have been placed in another. This is often the nature of work seeking to classify objects from the real world into neat groups.

In some cases there is uncertainty in the specifications of individual machines. Information on many of the products of long-defunct companies was available only through old articles, advertisements, and by recollections of those who used them. When these sources agree on the description of a particular machine it lends credence to the validity of the information. Occasionally there were discrepancies. Development of this guide is an ongoing process, and the information will be updated and appended to enhance the accuracy of future versions. The author welcomes input from any knowledgeable people, and can be contacted through the publisher. Along these same lines, some of the photographs in this catalog are from old advertisements, and occasionally are of poor quality. These will be systematically replaced by higher-quality photographs as more early machines are located and photographed. The author would appreciate assistance with this project from collectors possessing presentable machines.

I. HAND CALCULATORS

INTRODUCTION:

Hand-held calculators had their origins in the electronic desk-top calculators that began with the British Bell Punch in 1963. This large machine was comparable in size to a typewriter or cash-register, and used individual transistors instead of ICs. About 1967 Texas Instruments came out with a similar machine, only it employed ICs. In 1968, Hewlett-Packard introduced the 9100A, which could perform scientific calculations and which helped get Hewlett-Packard into the business of making computers. Many other companies followed these leads, and the technology yielded the pocket calculator. By 1971 mass-produced hand calculators were available. Aside from Hewlett-Packard and Texas Instruments, Commodore, a Canadian company, was one of the earlier hand-calculator manufacturers.

About 1974, intense competition in the hand-calculator market killed off many companies. The principle survivors were Hewlett-Packard, Texas Instruments, and various Japanese manufacturers. One of the companies forced out of the calculator market during this period was MITS. However, this led to MITS's subsequent development of the Altair 8800, and the spawning of the personal computer market.

HP-35, CREDIT: Photo Courtesy of Hewlett-Packard Company
HP (Hewlett-Packard) 35
Functions: Scientific.
Memories: 1.   (cont.)

1

Display: LED.
Production: Introduced in January 1972.
Cost: $395.

This was HP's first calculator, and the first of the tremendously-popular class of scientific calculators. It was known as the "electronic slide rule."

Value: $150-$250

TI (Texas Instruments) 2500 Datamath
Functions: Four.
Display: 8 LEDs.
Physical: 5.5-inches by 3.0 inches by 1.7 inches, weighs 12 ounces. Four-and-a-half hours battery life were claimed.
Production: Introduced September 21, 1972.
Cost: $119.95.

The TI-2500 was TI's first hand calculator. It was introduced along with the TI-3000 and TI-3500 desk-top calculators.

Value: $100-$175

HP-80, CREDIT: Photo Courtesy of Hewlett-Packard Company

HP 80
Functions: Business and finance.
Memories: 10.
Production: Introduced in January of 1973.
Cost: $395.

The HP-80 was the first strictly financial calculator.

Value: $15-$40

HP-45, CREDIT: Photo Courtesy of Hewlett-Packard Company

HP 45
Functions: Scientific.
Memories: 9.
Display: LED.
Production: Introduced in May of 1973.
Cost: $395.
The 45 was basically an advanced version of the HP 35.

Value: $75-$150

HP 46
Functions: 48, scientific.
Memories: 9.
Display: LED and paper printout.
Physical: A desk-top version of the 45.
The 46 was a printing scientific calculator. It was only offered for a brief time.

Value: $15-$25

TI (Texas Instruments) SR-11
Functions: Four, plus reciprocal, squares and roots.
Display: 12 LEDs.
Production: Announced September 11, 1973.
Cost: $119.95 initially, $79.95 later.
The SR-11 was like the SR-10, but with pi and a constant.

Value: $15-$25

3

TI SR-22
Functions: Four.
Display: LED.
Production: Announced on September 11, 1973.
The SR-22 hexadecimal calculator, it could convert between octal and decimal numbers.

Value: $15-$25

TI 2550
Functions: Four, plus percentage.
Memories: 1.
Production: Introduced on January 10, 1974.
Cost: $99.95, later down to $69.95.

Value: $10-$20

TI SR-50
Functions: Scientific.
Display: 14 LEDs.
Production: Announced on January 15, 1974.
Cost: $169.95.
The SR-50 was first marketed by direct mail.

Value: $20-$40

HP 65
Functions: Scientific.
Memories: 9.
Program steps: 100.
Display: LED.
Storage: Magnetic cards.
Physical: Weighed 11 ounces.
Cost: $795.
Production: Announced January 17, 1974.
Programs for this early programmable were sold in "PACs" of 40 cards each. By the end of 1975 there were 14 PACs available.

Value: $25-$50

TI 1500
Functions: Four, plus percent.
Display: 8 LEDs.
Physical: 5.0-inches by 2.6-inches by 1.0-inch.
Production: Introduced April 8, 1974.
Cost: $69.95, later lowered to $59.95.

Value: $10-$20

4

HP 70
Functions: Business.
Memories: 6.
Production: Introduced August of 1974.
Cost: $275.
The 70 was a business and finance calculator.

Value: $10-$20

TI SR-16
Display: 12 LEDs.
Production: Introduced on October 25, 1974.
Cost: $99.95.
The SR-6 was a Scientific calculator.

Value: $10-$20

TI 2250-II
Display: 8 LEDs.
Production: Introduced November 11, 1974.
Cost: $49.95.

Value: $10-$20

HP 55
Functions: 86, scientific.
Memories: 20.
Program steps: 49.
Display: LED.
Production: Introduced in January of 1975.
Cost: $395.
The 55 was an early programmable calculator. However, since it did not have continuous memory, programs were lost on power-down.

Value: $15-$25

Commodore 1400
Functions: Scientific.
Physical: 3¼-inches by 6-inches by 1¾-inches.
Production: In production by January 1975.

Value: $10-$20

HP 21
Functions: Scientific.
Display: 8-digit LEDs.
Production: Introduced in February of 1975.
Cost: $125.
The 21 was similar in performance to the earlier 35, which it replaced.
Value: $10-$20

Casio Mini Printer
Display: 8-digit LED.
Production: In production by March of 1975.
Cost: $129.95.
This machine had a built-in printer with unusual horizontal paper feed. It used 5/16-inch wide paper tape.

Value: $10-$20

Bowmar MX90
Functions: Included square-root.
Memories: 2.
Display: Ten digits.
Production: In production by March of 1975.

Value: $10-$15

Bowmar MX100
Production: In production by March of 1975.
Cost: $89.95.
A scientific calculator.

Value: $5-$15

HP 81
Functions: Business and finance.
Memories: 20.
Display: LED and paper printout.
Physical: Small desktop.
Production: In production by March of 1975.
This was an early printing calculator for business.

Value: $5-$15

Bowmar MX140
Functions: Scientific.
Display: Ten digits.
Production: In production by March of 1975.
Cost: $109.95.

Value: $5-$15

National Semiconductor Novus Mathematician
Production: In production by March of 1975.
Cost: $69.95.

Value: $5-$15

Kingsport SC40
Functions: Scientific, and had parenthesis.
Memories: Several.
Production: In production by March of 1975.
Cost: $99.95.

Value: $5-$15

Sinclair 105
Functions: Scientific.
Production: In production by March of 1975.
Cost: $39.95.

Value: $5-$15

TI 5050
Physical: 8.7-inches by 3.9-inches by 2.7-inches, weighed 28 ounces.
Production: Introduced on March 24, 1975.
Cost: $199.95.
The TI-5050 was a printing calculator. It printed on two-inch wide paper.
Value: $5-$10

TI SR-51
Functions: Scientific.
Memories: 10.
Display: LED.
Production: Introduced about March of 1975.
Cost: $224.95.

Value: $15-$25

TI 1250
Memories: 1.
Production: Introduced on June 1, 1975.
Cost: $24.95.

Value: $5-$10

TI 16II
Display: 12 LEDs.
Production: Introduced on August 1, 1975.
Cost: $49.95.

Value: $5-$10

HP 25
with case

HP 25
Functions: Scientific.
Memories: 8.
Program Steps: 49.
Production: Introduced in August of 1975.
Cost: $195.

Value: $10-$20

SR-52

TI SR-52
Functions: Scientific.
Memories: 22.
Program steps: 224.
Display: LED.
Storage: 2⅞-inch by ⅝-inch magnetic cards.
Physical: Weighed 12.3 ounces.
Cost: $395.
Production: Introduced September 16, 1975.

The SR-52 was an early and popular programmable scientific calculator.
An optional printer, the PC-100, was introduced January 7, 1976.

Value: $30-$60

HP 22
Functions: Financial.
Memories: 10.
Production: Introduced in September of 1975.
Cost: $165.
The HP-22 essentially replaced the HP-70.

Value: $10-$20

TI 2550 II
Functions: Four, plus square root, square, reciprocal, and percent.
Memories: 1.
Display: Vacuum-flourescent.
Physical: 5.8-inch by 3.2-inch by 1.25-inch, weighed about 8 ounces.
Production: Introduced on October 17, 1975.
Cost: $49.95.

Value: $5-$10

TI SR-56
Functions: Scientific.
Memories: 10.
Program steps: 100.
Production: Announced on January 21, 1976.
Cost: $179.95.

Value: $5-$10

HP 91
Functions: Scientific.
Memories: 16.
Display: LED.
Physical: Small desktop unit.
Cost: $500.
Production: Introduced in March of 1976.
This calculator was not programmable, but had a built-in printer. It was based on the HP-45.

Value: $15-$40

TI 1260
Production: Introduced on April 9, 1976.

Value: $5-$10

TI 1270
Functions: Four, plus reciprocal, square, square root, and pi.
Production: Introduced on April 21, 1976.
Cost: $1895.
The TI-1270 was designed for use in secondary schools.

Value: $5-$10

9

HP 27
Functions: Scientific and financial.
Memories: 10.
Production: Introduced in May of 1976.
Cost: $200.

Value: $10-$20

TI 1600
Production: Introduced on June 13, 1976.
Cost: $24.95.

Value: $5-$10

TI Business Analyst
Functions: Business.
Production: Introduced on June 13, 1976.
Cost: $49.95.

Value: $5-$10

TI Little Professor
Cost: $19.95 for the original version, $18.95 for the later, improved version.
Production: Introduced on June 13, 1976, an updated version with LCD display was introduced on January 5, 1982.
This device produced problems for children to answer, so it was not strictly a hand calculator.

Value: $15-$25

TI 1650
Production: Announced June 13, 1976.
Cost: $29.95.

Value: $5-$10

HP 25C
Functions: Scientific.
Memories: 8.
Program steps: 49.
Production: Introduced in July of 1976.
Cost: $200.
The HP-25C was basically the same as the HP-25, but it had continuous memory (retained when powered-down). This was HP's first model with this feature.

Value: $10-$20

HP 67
Functions: Scientific.
Memories: 26.
Program steps: 224.
Display: LED.
Storage: Magnetic cards.
Production: Introduced in July of 1976.
Cost: $450.
The 67 replaced the 65.

Value: $20-$50

HP 97
Functions: Scientific.
Memories: 26.
Program steps: 224.
Physical: Had a built-in printer.
Production: Introduced in July of 1976.
Cost: $750.
The 97 was basically a 67 with a built-in printer.

Value: $15-$40

National Semiconductor Novus 6030 Mathematician
Functions: Scientific.
Production: In production by 1976.

Value: $5-$10

Melcor SC-655
Functions: Scientific.
Memories: 12.
Production: In production by 1976.

Value: $5-$10

Monroe 360/65 Micro Bond Trader
Functions: Financial.
Production: In production by 1976.
The 360/65 was aimed at bond calculations.

Value: $10-$15

Commodore F4146R
Functions: Financial.
Display: 14 digits.
Production: In production by 1976.

Value: $10-$15

National Semiconductor Novus 6035 Programmable Mathematician
Functions: Scientific.
Production: In production by 1976.

Value: $5-$10

National Semiconductor Novus 6030 Statistician
Functions: Statistics.
Production: In production by 1976.

Value: $5-$10

National Semiconductor Novus 6035 Programmable Statistician
Functions: Statistics.
Productions: In production by 1976.

Value: $5-$10

National Semiconductor 4615
Functions: Scientific.
Program steps: 100.
Production: In production by 1976.
The 4615 operated in RPN.

Value: $5-$10

National Semiconductor 4640
Functions: Scientific, 54 functions.
Display: 12 LEDs.
Production: In production by 1976.
Cost: $89.95 in 1976.
The 4615 operated in RPN.

Value: $5-$10

Sinclair Scientific Programmable
Functions: Scientific.
Program steps: 24.
Production: In production by 1976.

Value: $5-$10

Litronix 2290
Functions: Four, plus square root.
Memories: 1.
Program steps: 10.
Display: LED.
Production: In production by 1976.
The 2290R was a rechargeable version of the 2290.

Value: $5-$10

Rockwell 44RD Electronic Slide Rule
Functions: Scientific.
Display: Green flourescent.
Production: In production by 1976.

Value: $5-$10

Rockwell 64RD Electronic Advanced Slide Rule
Functions: Scientific.
Memories: 1.
Display: 12 green flourescent digits.
Physical: 37 double-shot keys.
Production: In production by 1976.

Value: $5-$10

TI Money Manager
Production: Introduced on January 13, 1977.
Cost: $26.95.
The Money Manager was aimed at home finance calculations.

Value: $5-$10

TI 1750
Functions: Four, plus square root and percentages.
Display: LCD.
Physical: 4½-inches by 2¹¹⁄₁₆-inches by ⅜-inches, weighed less than 2.5 ounces.
Production: Introduced in mid-April of 1977.
Cost: $2495.

Value: $5-$10

TI 57
Program steps: 150.
Display: LED.
Cost: $79.95.
Production: Introduced on May 24, 1977.
The TI-57 superseded the SR-56.

Value: $5-$15

TI 58
Memories: 60.
Program steps: 480.
Display: LED.
Cost: $124.95.
Production: Introduced on May 24, 1977.

Value: $5-$15

TI 59
Memories: 100.
Program steps: 960.
Display: LED.
Storage: Magnetic cards.
Cost: $299.95.
Production: Introduced on May 24, 1977.
Modules containing programs with up to 5000 steps were available for this calculator. A magnetic card reader was available.

Value: $15-$25

TI MBA
Memories: 12.
Display: LED.
Cost: $79.95.
Production: Introduced on June 5, 1977.
This was an early business-oriented machine with several keys for standard business functions.

Value: $15-$30

TI DataMan!
Functions: Four.
Display: LED.
Cost: $24.95
Production: Introduced on June 5, 1977.
This calculator was designed for children to practice arithmetic or play math games. It was similar to the Little Professor.

Value: $25-$50

TI 1680
Display: 8 characters.
Production: Introduced on June 5, 1977.
Cost: $29.95.
The TI-1680 coud re-display up to 20 past numbers on its display, instead of having a printer.

Value: $5-$10

TI DataClip
Functions: Four.
Display: 12 vacuum-flourescent characters.
Physical: About the proportions of a six-inch ruler.
Production: Announced on June 5, 1977.
Cost: $34.95.

Value: $15-$30

14

HP 29C with case

HP 29C
Functions: Scientific.
Memories: 30.
Program steps: 98.
Production: Introduced in July of 1977.
Cost: $195.
The 29C was HP's second continuous memory calculator.

Value: $10-$20

HP 92
Functions: Financial.
Physical: Had a printer.
Production: Introduced in July of 1977.
Cost: $625.

Value: $5-$10

National Semiconductor Novus Scientist PR
Functions: Scientific.
Memories: 1.
Program steps: 100.
Display: Eight digit with two digit exponential LED display.
Physical: Powered by three AA NiCad batteries.
Cost: $89.95.
Production: In production by July of 1977.
This machine used RPN, 4-level stack, and scientific notation.

Value: $5-$15

HP 10
Functions: Four.
Memories: 1.
Production: Introduced in July of 1977.
Cost: $175.
This HP calculator had a printer. It differed from previous HP calculators in that it did not employ RPN, and hence had an "=" key.
Value: $10-$20

HP 01
Functions: Four.
Memories: 1.
Production: Introduced in July of 1977.
Cost: $650.
This watch-calculator told the time and date, as well as being a calculator. It had continuous memory.
Value: $25-$50

HP 19C
Production: Introduced in September of 1977.
Cost: $345.
The 19C was essentially the 29C with a built-in printer.
Value: $5-$10

TI 1790 DataChron
Display: LCD.
Production: Introduced January 5, 1978.
Cost: $50.
The DataChron calculator incorporated a watch with stopwatch and alarm.
Value: $5-$10

HP 31E
Functions: Scientific.
Memories: 4.
Production: Introduced in May of 1978.
Cost: $60.
The HP-31E replaced the HP-21.
Value: $5-$10

HP 33E
Functions: Scientific.
Memories: 8.
Program steps: 49.
Production: Introduced in May of 1978.
Cost: $100.
Value: $5-$10

HP 38E
Functions: Financial.
Memories: 20.
Program steps: 99.
Production: Introduced in May of 1978.
Cost: $120.
The HP-38E was the first financial calculator that coule be programmed.
Value: $5-$10

HP 32E
Functions: Scientific.
Memories: 15.
Production: Introduced in July of 1978.
Cost: $80.
The 32E had statistics functions and was HP's first calculator with hyperbolic functions.
Value: $5-$10

HP 37E
Functions: Financial.
Memories: 7.
Production: Introduced in July of 1978.
Cost: $75.
The HP-37E was the replacement for the HP-22.
Value: $5-$10

HP 33C
Functions: Scientific.
Memories: 8.
Program steps: 49.
Production: Introduced in July of 1979.
Cost: $120.
The 33C was basically the 33E, but with continuous memory.
Value: $5-$10

HP 34C
Functions: Scientific.
Memories: 21.
Program steps: 210.
Production: Introduced in July of 1979.
Cost: $150.
The HP-34C was a replacement for the HP-29C.
Value: $5-$10

HP 38C
Functions: Financial.
Memories: 20.
Program steps: 99.
Production: Introduced in July of 1979.
Cost: $150.

The HP-38C was basically the HP-38E with continuous memory.
Value: $5-$10

II-1. HOBBYIST HOME COMPUTERS

These machines were the first personal computers. Typically aimed at hobbyists, rather than those with serious need of a computer, they were often sold as kits. In many cases, completion of the kit was just a starting point for the hobbyist to build from, as the basic configurations the kits supplied were very minimal. Programming was often in assembly language or BASIC, and most owners were programmers themselves, even if they did use commercial software. Nonetheless, it is from these rudimentary beginnings that the personal computer market got its start.

Geniac
Processor: Proprietary.
RAM: None.
Display: Incandescent lights.
Operator input: Through rotating the disk insulator.
Data storage: None.
Physical: Constructed from rotating fiberboard disks using bolts for contacts. Ran on dry-cell batteries.
Production: In production by fall of 1956.
Cost: $12.95 for the kit.

Sold primarily as a toy, this type of machine was arguably the first digital personal computer. It was programmed by changing the wiring of the contacts (which were bolts). There were two sets of contacts, one located around the periphery of a rotating disk, and the other on a baseboard on which the disk was mounted. It was operated by rotating the disk. Able to only do a few simple tasks, such as changing the base of a number from two to 16, it nonetheless was digital and programmable, and hence qualifies as a personal computer.

Value: $400-$600

Scelbi Computer Consulting 8H
Processor: Intel 8008.
Production: Introduced in 1973.

Predating the Altair, this scarce machine was made in small quantities.
Value: $1500-$2000

Mark-8
Processor: Intel 8008.
RAM: 256 bytes, expandable to 16 K.
Display: Panel of lights.
Operator input: Toggle switches.
Data storage: None.
Physical: Breadbox-sized.
Production: Introduced in July of 1974, production likely ran 1000 to 2000.
Cost: The complete machine cost about $250. The instructions sold for $5.50 and the circuit boards were $47.50.

This is the first personal computer to really be marketed. Sold as kit only, this machine had no ROM.
Value: $8000-$11,000

MITS (Micro Instrumentation and Telemetry Systems) Altair 8800
Processor: Intel 8080, running at 2 MHz.
RAM: 256 bytes intially standard. 1,024 and 4,096 boards were soon available.
Data storage: Paper tape or cassette initially, later floppy disks.
Physical: S-100 backplane bus in a metal box.
Production: The 8800 was announced in January 1975 but was not shipping by April. Production did not really get going until summer, but by the end of the year over 5000 had been shipped. MITS was sold to Pertec on May 22, 1977, and in about two years it failed.
Cost: Prices were initially $395 as a kit and $650 assembled, but later in production were $439 as a kit and $621 assembled.

This was the first mass-marketed personal computer and originator of the S-100 bus standard. Due to its relatively high production, it is likely the earliest really collectible personal computer. This machine is considered by many to be the first true microcomputer.

Value: $800-$1200

Processor Technology Corp SOL System 1
Processor: Intel 8080A.
RAM: 10 K.
Operator input: Integral keyboard.
Data storage: Cassette and floppy drive.
Production: The company started in April of 1975.
Cost: $1649 as a kit, $2129 assembled.

This was an S-100 machine, following closely after the Altair.

Value: $300-$500

Processor Technology Corp. SOL-20
Processor: Intel 8080A.
RAM: 1 K, expandable to 64 K.
Display: Came with video display circuitry standard, and a monitor
was optional.
Display: Came with video display circuitry standard, and a monitor
was optional.
Operator input: 85-key keyboard.
Data storage: An audio cassette interface was standard and a dual
floppy system was optional.
Physical: Weighed 42 pounds and had a walnut-sided case.
Production: The SOL line was introduced about April of 1975.
Cost: $995 as a kit, $1495 assembled, $475 as a board only.

*This S-100 machine had five expansion slots, one serial port and one parallel
port. BASIC-5 was available on cassette, as well as several space games.*
Value: $300-$500

Processor Technology Corp SOL-10
Processor: Intel 8080A.
Display: CRT could display the full 128 upper and lower case ASCII
character set.
Data storage: Cassette interface.
Production: In production by January of 1977.
Cost: $795.

*This machine was the same as the SOL-20, but the SOL-20 had a heavier-
duty power supply and a backplane for five extra S-100 cards. It had both
serial and 8-bit parallel ports.*
Value: $275-$450

MOS Technology Kim-1
Processor: 6502.
RAM: 1,024 bytes, expandable on the board to 4 K.
Display: Six-digit octal LED display.
Operator input: 23-key octal keyboard.
Data storage: An audio cassette interface was available.
Physical: A 10.75-inch by 8.875-inch single-board computer.
Production: Introduced first in 1975. Was bought out by Commodore
in October 1976.
Cost: Initially sold for $245, but later dropped to $169.95 (including
the power supply).

*This single-board computer came as a completely assembled mother board,
but without a power supply. The software was contained in 2,048 bytes
of ROM. This was an interesting machine for several reasons: it was
assembled, not as a kit, and was the first case of a semiconductor manufacturer bringing out their own microcomputer, hence validating the
microcomputer market. In addition, with the Commodore buy-out, it
represented the first case of an established company in the electronics
business producing a microcomputer.*
Value: $125-$175 for "MOS"-marked version, **$100-$150** for "Commodore"-
marked version.

Scelbi Computer Consulting 8B
Processor: Intel 8008.
RAM: 4 K, expandable to 16 K.
Display: An interface was available to allow an oscilloscope to act as an alphanumeric display.
Operator input: Both keyboard and Teletype interfaces were available.
Data storage: An audio cassette interface was available.
Production: Delivery began in June 1975.
Cost: $259 for unpopulated cards and chassis kit. Kits complete with 1,024 bytes RAM available for $449. Available assembled with 4,096 bytes RAM for $849.

Value: $800-$1200

The successor to the pioneer 8H.

Sphere 1
Processor: Motorola 6800.
RAM: 4 K
Display: CRT.
Operator input: Keyboard.
Data storage: Cassette.
Production: Introduced in 1975.
Cost: $650 for the "hobbyist" machine with 4 K and keyboard. $750 for the "intelligent" machine with a 16-line by 32-character display, a built in modem and audio cassette interface. $1345 for the "basic" machine with BASIC, 20 K bytes, 512 character CRT, keyboard, modem, and cassette interface.

A 1024-byte PROM allowed programming to be done by a keyboard, so front-panel switches and LEDs were no longer needed. The literature was written for the businessman, not the computer expert.

Value: $200-$300

24

Sphere 2
Processor: Motorola 6800.
RAM: 4 K, expandable to 16 K.
Display: Could drive a 512 display on a standard television.
Operator input: Keyboard.
Data storage: Cassette.
Production: In production by January of 1976.
Cost: $999 as a kit, $1499 assembled.

The Sphere 2 was similar to the Sphere 1, but it had serial communication port and an audio cassette or MODEM interface.

Value: $200-$300

Sphere 3
Processor: Motorola 6800.
RAM: 4 K, expandable to 16 K.
Display: Could drive a 512 display on a standard television.
Operator input: Keyboard.
Data storage: Cassette.
Production: In production by January of 1976.
Cost: $1765 as a kit, $2250 assembled.

The Sphere 3 was similar to the Sphere 2, but it had 20 K additional memory.

Value: $200-$300

Sphere 4
Processor: Motorola 6800.
RAM: 4 K, expandable to 16 K.
Display: Could drive a 512 display on a standard television.
Operator input: Keyboard.
Data storage: Dual IBM-compatible floppy disks instead of the cassette of the models 1 to 3.
Production: In production by January of 1976.
Cost: $6100 as a kit, $7995 assembled.

The Sphere 4 was similar to the Sphere 3, but it included a disk-operating system with BASIC and a 65 LPM line printer.

Value: $200-$300

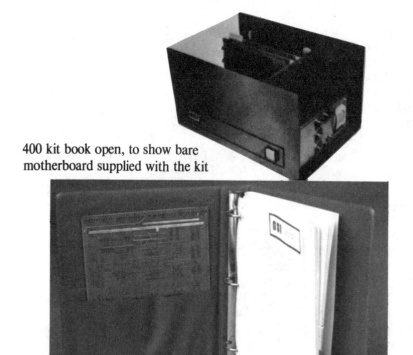

400 kit book open, to show bare motherboard supplied with the kit

OSI (Ohio Scientific Instruments) Challenger 400
Processor: 6502A, running at 2 MHz, or 6502C, running at 4 MHz.
RAM: 1,024 bytes, with 4 K expansion, later, 16 K expandable to 192 K.
Display: Had video graphics board with alphabetics, graphics and color. Later, a Sanyo monitor was available, with displays of 16 lines by 64 characters per line.
Data storage: Cassette ($89), single floppy drive ($990), dual floppy drive ($1490). Later standard with floppy drive.
Production: Available since November 1975, and with floppy since June 1976. Still in production by May 1977.
Cost: $439 to $675, depending on configuration. Later, $2599 with terminal and monitor, or $2099 without.

The challenger came with BASIC and one serial port. It also came as a kit comprised of a motherboard inside the front pocket of a blue OSI three-ring notebook containing instructions and specification sheets for the machine.
Value: $150-$225 for the assembled machine with OSI case, **$100-$200** for the notebook with motherboard.

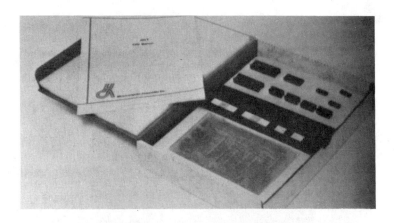

Microcomputer Associates Jolt
Processor: MOS Tech 6502.
RAM: 512 bytes on the card, 4 K card available for $265 as a kit or $320 assembled.
Production: Introduced about December of 1975.
Cost: $249 as a kit, $348 assembled.

This kit had a serial interface to the terminal and a monitor in ROM.
                                                        Value: $150-$250

Sphere One-Card Computer
Processor: Motorola 6800.
RAM: 4 K.
Production: In production by December of 1975.
Cost: $350 as a kit, $520 assembled.

Value: $125-$200

RGS Electronics 008A
Processor: Intel 8008.
RAM: 1 K, 2 K board kit available.
Display: Row of LEDs.
Operator input: Rocker switches, but ASCII keyboard kit was available for $135.
Data storage: A cassette tape adaptor was available for $100.
Production: In production in fall of 1975.
Cost: Sold as a kit for $375.

This kit had six PC boards, components, a front panel, 1 K of RAM and a power supply. No cabinet was included. As with many early machines, the processor and control circuitry were mounted on boards plugged into the main board. A parallel interface was available for $43.75. This was the first 8008 machine reviewed by Byte.

Value: $150-$250

Martin Research   Mike 203A (Mike 2)
Processor: Intel 8008.
RAM: A 4 K board with 450 ns static RAM was available at $165 as a kit, or $190 assembled.
Display: Had six octal digits in a seven-segment display.
Operator input: 20-pad keyboard.
Production: In production by September of 1975.
Cost: $270 as a kit, $345 assembled.

This board-level kit initially came without a standard cabinet or power supply. It's keyboard and octal display were touted as a great improvement over LEDs and toggle switches.

Value: $75-$125

Martin Research   Mike 303A (Mike 3)
Processor: Intel 8080.
RAM: 256 K standard, 4 K board with 450 ns static RAM available at $165 as a kit, or $190 assembled.
Display: Six octal in a seven-segment display.
Operator input: 20-pad keyboard.
Production: In production by September of 1975.
Cost: $395 as a kit, $495 assembled.

This was a board-level kit without cabinet or power supply. It's keyboard and octal display were touted as a great improvement over LEDs and toggle switches.

Value: $75-$125

SWTCP (Southwest Technical Products Corp.) 6800
Processor: Motorola MC6800.
RAM: 2 K, expandable to 64 K.
Display: CT-1024 video terminal was available.
Operator input: Any ASCII terminal.
Data storage: Paper tape, cassette or floppy disk.
Production: Introduced about November of 1975.
Cost: Prices of the basic kit begin at $450 initially, but fell to about $345 later.

This machine was available as a kit only. It ran the Mikbug ROM operating system, and could be had with RS-232 or 20 mA TTY interfaces for $35.
Value: $150-$225

late 680

early 680

MITS (Micro Instrumentation and Telemetry Systems) Altair 680
Processor: Motorola 6800.
RAM: 1,024 bytes.
Display: Row of LEDs, but CRTs were soon available.
Operator input: Toggle switches, but various terminals and keyboards were soon available.
Physical: 11" by 11" 4 11/16", about one-third the size of the 8800.
Production: Introduced in December 1975.
Cost: Sold initially at an introductory kit price of $293, it had the lowest price of any complete computer. Normal costing was $345 as a kit and $420 assembled.

MIT's move to cover the 6800 market, the machine was small and less expensive than its older brother the 8800. Various S-100 cards were available by MITS and others.

Value: $400-$800

Comp-Sultants   Micro-440
Processor: Intel 4040.
RAM: 256 bytes, with room for up to 8 K.
Display: LEDs.
Operator input: Switches.
Cost: $275 as a kit, $375 assembled.
Production: In production by December of 1975.

This very early machine was likely the first Intel 4040 kit.

Value: $150-$250

SWTPC (Southwest Techical Products Corp.) MP-68
Processor: Motorola MC6800.
RAM: 2 K to 4 K.
Display: TTY or RS-232C ASCII terminal.
Operator input: TTY or RS-232C ASCII terminal.
Production: In production by December of 1975.
Cost: $450.

This machine had RS-232C or 20 mA current loop interfaces, and a 1 K ROM operating system.

Value: $100-$200

Systems Research SRI-500
Processor: Mostek F-8.
RAM: 1 K.
Display: SRI-520 video interface was optional for $175.
Operator input: SRI-510 keyboard was optional for $125.
Data storage: SRI-530 cassette interface optional for $75.
Cost: $575.
Production: In production by January of 1976.

Had both RS-232 and TTY I/Os.   **Value: $75-$125**

Systems Research   Little Byte SRI-1000
Processor: National Semiconductor PACE.
RAM: 4 K, expandable.
Display: Optional video interface.
Operator input: Keyboard.
Data storage: Had a cassette interface, and a floppy disk was optional.
Cost: $559 assembled.
Production: In production by December of 1975.

*Modem, RS-232, TTY, TTL and parallel interfaces were optional, as was
a line printer.*   **Value: $75-$125**

INSAI (IMS Associates, Inc.) 8080
Processor: Intel 8080A.
RAM: 4 K, expandable to 64 K.
Display: LEDs.
Operator input: Toggle switches.
Data storage: Floppy drive and a 50 M hard drive were available.
Physical: Lucite front panel and an aluminum case.
Production: In production by December of 1975.
Cost: Initially $439 as a kit, $931 assembled, with 1 K RAM.

This early Altair clone machine was at one time the fastest-selling microcomputer. It had an S-100 bus with 22 expansion slots.
Value: $150-$225

Wave Mate   Jupiter II
Processor: Motorola MC6800.
RAM: 8 K.
Display: Teletype or television.
Operator input: Teletype.
Data storage: Dual audio cassette drives were available.
Production: Introduced about January of 1976.
Cost: $1225 introductory kit price, $1885 assembled.

Has system monitor and debug programs in ROM. Came with a text editor, assembler and BASIC.

Value: $125-$200

DEC (Digital Equipment Corp.) LSI-11
RAM: 4 K.
Operator input: ASCII consol.
Physical: 3.5"H by 19"W by 13.5"D.
Production: In production by early 1976.

This 16-bit microcomputer was "not intended to be a low end minicomputer, but to provide minicomputer capability to the new microcomputer applications." It used standard PDP-11 software, and has serial and parallel interfaces available.

Value: $150-$250

ISC (Intelligent Systems Corp.) Intercolor 8001
Processor: Intel 8080A.
RAM: 4 K standard, expandable up to 32 K.
Display: An 8-color 19-inch CRT with 25 lines by 80 characters per line.
Operator input: Keyboard.
Data storage: 5.25-inch floppy drive.
Production: Introduced in early 1976.
Cost: Ranged from $1395 to $1495.
Comments: A light-pen was optional with this integrated desk-top system. Had PROM software.

Value: $75-$125

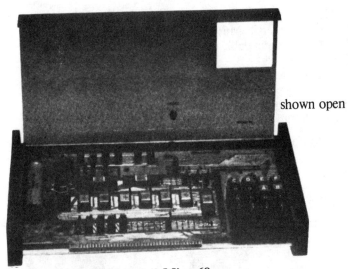

shown open

EPA (Electronic Product Associates) Micro68
Processor: Motorola/AMI 6800.
RAM: Could be expanded to 64 K. An 8 K RAM board was available for $270.
Display: Came with integral display.
Operator input: Had an integral keyboard.
Production: In production by early 1976.
Cost: $430 assembled.

Had a Samsonite carrying case.   **Value: $100-$150**

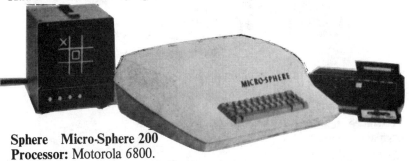

Sphere   Micro-Sphere 200
Processor: Motorola 6800.
RAM: 4 K, expandable to 8 K.
Display: Used a standard TV, which could be supplied as an option. Had graphics capability.
Operator input: Keyboard and optional graphics device (a "mouse").
Data storage: Could drive up to three cassette recorders.
Production: Was in production by March of 1976.
Cost: $860 assembled.

Billed as a low-cost machine.   **Value: $150-$250**

PCM 12
Processor: Intersil IM6100.
RAM: 4 K, expandable to 32 K.
Display: LEDs.
Operator input: Toggle switches.
Data storage: Audio cassette recorder interface.
Production: Introduced about March of 1976.
Cost: $400 to $600, depending on options.

Its software was compatible with the DEC PDP-8/E minicomputer. A serial terminal interface came with the complete kit.

Value: $125-$200

Viatron System 21 Data Management Station
Display: Video monitor.
Operator input: Keyboard.
Data storage: Dual tape decks.
Production: Available to the personal computer market by March of 1976.

This machine was sold "as is" by Meshna of Lynn, Massachusetts. The machines were unused, but "due to 4 years of storage, may require some adjusting/cleaning." It had two I/O channels and hard-wired programs.

Value: $125-$200

PolyMorphic Systems   Micro-Altair
Processor: Intel 8080.
RAM: 512 bytes.
Display: Required a TV monitor.
Operator input: Required a keyboard.
Production: Introduced about April of 1976.
Cost: $592 as a kit, but was offered at $475 as a special introductory
offer up to April 15, 1976.

*Several CPU boards could be plugged into the backplane for parallel
processing.*

Value: $150-$225

EBKA Industries Familiarizor
Processor: MOS Technology 6502.
RAM: 1 K byte.
Display: Hex.
Operator input: Hex keyboard.
Production: In production about April 1976.

*The keyboard and display of this machine were built-in to a single PC board,
and it had a 256-byte monitor in PROM. It had two 8-bit I/O ports, one
input and one output.*

Value: $100-$175

Mikra-D VT1920
Processor: Intel 8080.
Display: CRT terminal with 80-character by 24-line display.
Operator input: Keyboard on terminal.
Production: In production by April of 1976.
Cost: $695 a kit.

Value: $100-$150

Mikra-D MTS-8
Processor: Intel 8080.
RAM: 4 K.
Display: CRT terminal with 80-character by 24-line display.
Operator input: Keyboard on terminal.
Production: In production by April of 1976.
Cost: $1195 as a kit.

The MTS-8 was similar to the VT-1920, but it had 1 K of ROM, serial interface, and assembler editor and debugging software.

Value: $100-$150

Mikra-D BASIC-8
Processor: Intel 8080.
RAM: 4 K.
Display: CRT terminal with 80-character by 24-line display.
Operator input: Keyboard on terminal.
Production: In production by April of 1976.
Cost: $1695 as a kit.

The BASIC-8 was similar to the MTS-8, but it had additional RAM and BASIC.

Value: $100-$150

HAL Communications MCEM-8080
Processor: Intel 8080.
RAM: 1024, expandable to 2 K.
Display: CRT optional.
Operator input: Keyboard optional.
Data storage: Audio cassette was optional.
Production: In production by May of 1976.
Cost: $375.

This was a single-board computer. It had TTY and three parallel I/Os.
Value: $50-$100

Intersil IM6100
Processor: Intersil IM6100, running at 4 MHz.
Production: In production by May of 1976.

This derivative of the DEC PDP-8/E had a serial interface. It could run on a subset of the PDP-8 OMNIBUS, a 12-bit data bus for address and data information.
Value: $100-$150

Technical Design Labs   Xitan alpha 1
Processor: Zilog Z-80.
RAM: 2 K.
Display: Could drive a CRT.
Data storage: Cassette.
Production: In production by June of 1977.
Cost: $769 as a kit, $1039 assembled.

This machine had six expansion slots.
Value: $100-$150

Technical Design Labs   Xitan alpha 2
Processor: Zilog Z-80.
RAM: 2 K to 16 K.
Data storage: 1200-Baud cassette interface.
Production: In production by June of 1976.
Cost: $1369 as a kit, $1749 assembled.

This S-100 machine was the same as the Alpha 1, but it had the "Z16" memory module added. It had one parallel and two serial ports.

Value: $100-$150

Data General microNOVA
Processor: microNOVA mN601.
RAM: Up to 32 K.
Production: Was introduced about June of 1976.

This microcomputer had a similar architecture to the Data General NOVA minicomputers. It was primarily oriented toward the OEM systems and integration markets.

Value: $125-$175

Apple I
Processor: 6502.
RAM: 4 K, expandable to 8 K.
Display: Could drive a TV.
Production: About 200 of this predecessor of the important Apple II were made. It was designed in late 1975, and production began in July of 1976.
Cost: $666.66.

This machine had great historical importance as the progenitor of the Apple computer line. It is well-recognized as a collector's item.
Value: $8000 to $12,000, but there have been reports of these machines selling for over $20,000.

PolyMorphic Systems   Poly 88
Processor: Intel 8080 or 8080A running at 1.853 MHz.
RAM: Ranged from 512 bytes to 16 K. 8 K was available for $300 as a kit or $375 assembled.
Display: Could drive a TV monitor. The VIT/32 32 character/line driver was available for $160 as a kit or $230 assembled.
Operator input: Required a keyboard.
Data storage: A cassette option was available.
Physical: 6.75"H by 4.25"W by 17"D.
Production: Production began in mid-1976.
Cost: $575 as a kit, $795 assembled.

Formerly called MICRO-ALTAIR, this machine had a video driver, debugger and a 1024-byte monitor in ROM. It used the S-100 bus and had five expansion slots.

Value: $100-$150

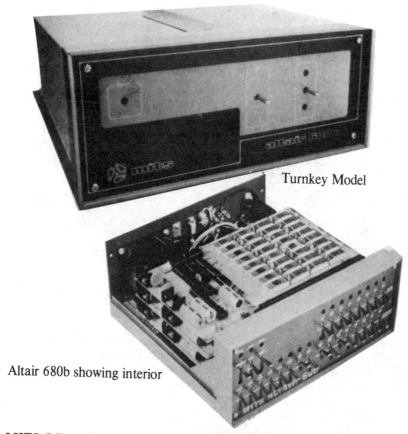

Turnkey Model

Altair 680b showing interior

MITS (Micro Instrumentation and Telemetry Systems) Altair 680b
Processor: 6800 running at 500 KHz.
RAM: 16 K static memory card available, 215 nS. The system could hold three 16 K cards.
Display: LEDs.
Operator input: Row of switches.
Data storage: Cassette.
Physical: 11 1/16"W by 11 1/16"D by 4 11/16"H.
Production: Work began on this machine in late 1975. It was in production in 1976.
Cost: $466 as a kit, $625 assembled.

This was one of the last MITS computers. It could be bought by time payments, and almost all circuitry was on a single large board. It had RS-232, TTY, and 20 mA current loop interfaces.

Value: $275-$350

Veras F-8
RAM: 1 K, expandable to 65 K, 4 K boards available.
Physical: 7" by 16" by 14 3/4".
Cost: $429 as kit, $675 assembled, later $459 and $709.
Production: In production by mid-1976.

The F-8 had both parallel and serial ports.

Value: $125-$175

AMT (Applied Microtechnology) 2650
Processor: Signetics 2650.
RAM: 256 bytes.
Display: LED displays.
Operator input: Toggle switches.
Cost: $195 assembled, power supply optional at $39.95.
Production: Announced in summer of 1976.

The 2650 was a single-board system for learning computers.

Value: $50-$100

8800a interior view

MITS (Micro Instrumentation and Telemetry Systems) Altair 8800a
Processor: Intel 8080A.
Production: Was in production by October of 1976.
Cost: $539.

Value: $300-$375

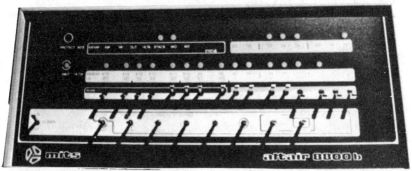

MITS Altair 8800b

Processor: Intel 8080A running at 2 MHz.
RAM: Could have up to 64 K.
Display: Had the same LED arrangement as the Altair 8800, but with a "new back-lit Duralith (laminated plastic and Mylar, bonded to aluminum) dress panel with multi-color graphics."
Operator input: Had the same switch arrangement as the Altair 8800, but with "new longer, flat toggle switches."
Data storage: Cassette of floppy drive.
Production: In production by fall 1976.
Cost: $840 as a kit, $1100 assembled.   **Value: $250-$350**

This machine was an improved version of the 8800.

Astral 2000

Processor: 6800.
RAM: 8 K, 500 ns. More 8 K boards available for $245 each.
Display: LEDs. Also the VID-80 video terminal board was available (at $189.95 as a kit or $245 assembled).
Operator input: Toggle switches.
Data storage: A tape interface was available for $49.95. A floppy disk controller was planned to be introduced by the last quarter of 1976 for under $1000.
Production: Introduced about October of 1976.
Cost: $995 as a kit, $1250 assembled.

Software for the 2000 was available on paper or magnetic tape, and an Astral BASIC was available. It had a 16 K monitor in ROM, and an RS-232 and 20 mA I/Os on the processor board.   **Value: $150-$250**

Electronic Tool Co. ETC-1000
Processor: 6502
Display: 8-digit display.
Operator input: 40-key keyboard with full set of hex keys.
Production: In production by October of 1976.
Cost: $675.

*This machine was intended for system development, control and small-scale
data processing, this system was sold assembled. It had 256 bytes of ROM.
A 20 mA current loop was standard, and an RS-232 was optional.*
Value: $100-$150

Digital   The Digital Group
Processor: Different systems offered different processors, including In-
tel 8080, Motorola 6800, Zilog Z-80, and MOS Tech 6500. CPU cards
were interchangeable.
RAM: 1 K.
Display: Video monitor.
Operator input: Keyboard.
Physical: Housed in an 1/8-inch thick anodized aluminum case in
"computer beige with chocolate brown." The cases were designed to
give all the Digital Group products a similar appearance.
Production: In production by October of 1976.
Cost: Prices started at $645 for the Z-80 system.   **Value: $100-$150**

Cromemco Z-1
Processor: Zilog Z-80 running at 4 MHz or 2 MHz.
RAM: 8 K.
Display: Rows of lights.
Operator input: By switches, with keyboard optional.
Physical: 7"H by 19.5"W by 17"D.
Production: Announced about December of 1976.
Cost: $2495.

*This S-100 machine had 21 expansion slots and an RS-232 interface. It was
not a kit. The CPU cards could be changed, and it had a cooling fan.*
Value: $150-$225

Terak 8510
Processor: LSI-11.
RAM: 20 K words of 16 bit memory.
Data storage: 256 K floppy drive.
Production: Introduced about January of 1977.
Cost: Slightly over $5000.

The 8510 had RS-232 and 20 mA current loop serial interfaces. Software included BASIC and FORTRAN.

Value: $75-$125

Cybersystems   Microcyber 1000
Processor: 6502.
RAM: Up to 64 K.
Display: CRT.
Operator input: 23-key keyboard.
Data storage: Cassette.
Physical: 14" by 11" by 2".
Production: In production by February of 1977.
Cost: $525.

The Microcyber 1000 had both TTY 20 mA and RS-232C serial interfaces, a 16-bit address bus and an 8-bit data bus.

Value: $100-$150

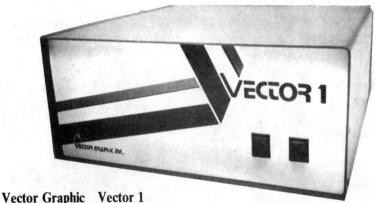

Vector Graphic   Vector 1
Processor: Intel 8080A.
RAM: 1 K.
Data storage: Cassette or floppy disk.
Production: Was in production by February of 1977.
Cost: $619 as a kit, $849 assembled.

This was an S-100 machine with 18 expansion slots.

Value: $125-$175

ECD MicroMind I
Processor: 6512A.
RAM: 8 K.
Data storage: Cassette.
Production: In production by 1977.
Cost: $987.54.   **Value: $75-$125**

PolyMorphic Systems   Poly 88 System 16
Processor: Intel 8080A.
RAM: 16 K.
Display: 9-inch CRT.
Data storage: Cassette.
Production: In production by 1977.
Cost: $2250.

S-100 machines, the Poly 88 Systems 1 to 7 came in increasingly complex packages:
Sys 1:8080, ½ K ram, could display 16 lines of 32 characters each on video interface, keyboard input port, $595.
Sys 2: same as 1, plus cassette interface kit and 64 character line option, $690.
Sys 3: same as 2, plus 8 K ram, basic and assembler on tape, $990.
Sys 4: same as 3, plus TV, keyboard, cassette recorder and cables, $1350.
Sys 7: same as 4, but was assembled.

It was claimed that these machines could be put together in three evenings.
                                                    Value: $125-$200

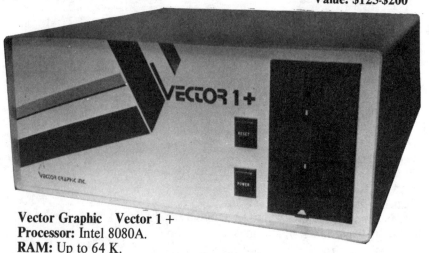

Vector Graphic   Vector 1 +
Processor: Intel 8080A.
RAM: Up to 64 K.
Data storage: Built-in 5.25-inch floppy drive.
Production: In production by 1977.
Cost: $659.
This was an S-100 machine with 18 expansion slots.   **Value: $100-$150**

PolyMorphic Systems   Poly 88 System 6
Processor: 8080A.
RAM: 16 K.
Data storage: Cassette.
Production: In production by 1977.
Cost: $1575 as a kit.

This was an S-100 bus machine.

Value: $125-$200

ECD   MicroMind II
Processor: 6512A.
RAM: 16 K.
Data storage: Cassette.
Production: In production by 1977.
Cost: $1287.54.

Value: $75-$125

HAL Communications Eight thousand
Processor: Intel 8080A.
RAM: 9 K.
Data Storage: Cassette.
Production: In production by 1977.
Cost: Less than $1500.

This machine came with one parallel port.

Value: $50-$100

Wave Mate   Jupiter IIC
Processor: Motorola 6800.
RAM: 8 K.
Data Storage: Cassette or floppy drive.
Production: In production by 1977. Still in production by 1979.
Cost: $2850 as a kit, $3500 assembled.

Value: $100-$175

Electronic Control Tech   ECT-100-Z80
Processor: Zilog Z-80.
Production: In production in 1977.
Cost: $420 as a kit, $600 assembled.

The ECT-100-Z80 was an S-100 bus machine.

Value: $100-$150

Digital   Digital Group, System 3
Processor: Zilog Z-80.
RAM: 18 K.
Data storage: Cassette.
Production: In production in 1977.
Cost: $2045 as a kit, $2545 assembled.

Value: $75-$125

Cromemco Z-2
Processor: Zilog Z-80, running at 4 MHz.
Physical: 12.25"H by 19"W by 20.75"D.
Production: In production by March of 1977.
Cost: $595 as a kit, $995 assembled.

Z-2K was the kit and Z-2W was the assembled machine. Each had an S-100 bus, and 21 expansion slots.

Value: $125-$200

Wave Mate   Jupitor IIIC
Processor: Zilog Z-80.
RAM: 8 K.
Data storage: Cassette or floppy drive.
Production: Available in 1977.
Cost: $2620 kit, $3570 assembled.

Value: $100-$150

AMI   EVK 99
Processor: Motorola 6800.
RAM: 16 K available for $77.95.
Production: In production by April of 1977.

This machine consisted of a board only. No keyboard or display was included.

Value: $50-$100

Realistic Controls Z//100-1
Processor: Intel 8080.
RAM: 33 K, expandable to 64 K.
Display: CRT available.
Data storage: Dual IBM-compatible floppy drive.
Production: In production by May of 1977.
Cost: $7995.

A FORTRAN compiler was available for the 100-1.

Value: $100-$150

Realistic Controls Z//100-2
Processor: Intel 8080.
RAM: 33 K, expandable to 64 K.
Display: CRT available.
Data storage: Dual IBM-compatible floppy drive.
Production: In production by May of 1977.
Cost: $8995

This machine was available with a FORTRAN compiler. It came with a 60-cps line printer.

Value: $100-$150

Realistic Controls Z//100-3
Processor: Intel 8080.
RAM: 33 K, expandable to 64 K.
Display: 120-character CRT.
Operator input: Keyboard.
Data storage: Dual IBM-compatible floppy drive.
Production: In production by May of 1977.
Cost: $9795.

A FORTRAN compiler was available for the 100-3, as was a 300 lines/min. line printer. This machine had an RS-232-C I/O.

Value: $100-$150

North Star Horizon
Processor: Zilog Z-80 running at 4 MHz.
RAM: 16 K, expandable to 64 K in 16 K steps.
Display: 24-line by 80-character upper and lower case video display controller board was available.
Operator input: Numeric keypad.
Data storage: One or two 5.25-inch Shugart floppy drive built-in. A hard drive was available later.
Physical: Was "offered in choice of wood or blue metal cover at no extra charge."
Production: Introduced about November of 1977.
Cost: The single drive unit was $1599 as a kit, or $1899 assembled. The dual drive unit was $1999 as a kit, or $2349 assembled.

This S-100 machine had 12 expansion slots and a serial interface.
Value: $100-$150

Microkit 8/16 Universal Microcomputer Development System
Processor: Intel 8080 and Motorola 6800 versions available.
RAM: 32 K.
Display: CRT.
Data storage: Dual cassette recorders.
Production: Introduced in July of 1977.
Cost: $5275.

Value: $100-$150

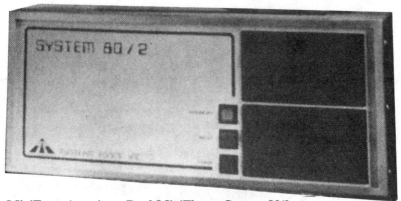

MiniTerm Associates Dual MiniFloppy System 80/2
Processor: Zilog Z-80.
Data storage: Two mini-floppies.
Production: In production by August 1977.

Advertising of this S-100 machine was aimed at the business market.
Value: $100-$150

IMSAI (IMS Associates, Inc.) Megabyte Micro
Production: In production by August of 1977.

This S-100 machine included a "time of day" clock.
Value: $125-$200

MSI (Midwest Scientific Instruments) 6800
Processor: Motorola 6800 running at speeds up to 2 MHz.
RAM: 8 K.
Data storage: MSI FD-8 floppy drive available.
Production: Introduced at Personal Computing show at the end of
August 1977 in Atlantic City.

BASIC was available on an 8-inch floppy drive.
Value: $100-$150

RCA Cosmac VIP (Video Interface Processor)
Processor: RCA CDP-1802.
RAM: Initially 2 K expandable to 4 K, later 4 K expandable to 32 K.
Display: Three LEDs, but could drive TV.
Operator input: 16-key hexadecimal keypad. 128-key ASCII keyboard available.
Data storage: Could drive a cassette.
Physical: 8.5"-by-11" circuit card.
Production: In production by August of 1977.
Cost: Initially $275, falling later to less than $250.

This kit included a board only, and was an inexpensive hobby computer. It evolved from the 1974 FRED computer.

Value: $75-$125

Technico   TEC-9900-SS
Processor: TMS9900.
RAM: Expandable up to 65 K.
Production: In production by August of 1977.
Cost: $299 as a kit, $399 assembled.
This was a one-board computer.

Value $50-$100

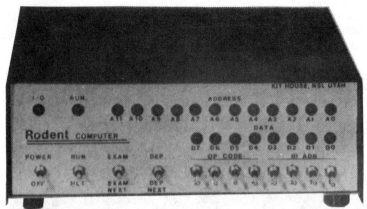

Kit House Rodent
RAM: A kit to give 3 K of RAM was available for $99.
Production: In production in August 1977.
Cost: $129 as a kit.
The Rodent came with a parallel port.　　　　　　　**Value: $125-$175**

Ebnek 77
Processor: TI TMS9900 running at 3 MHz.
RAM: 16 K expandable to 128 K.
Display: TV with 15 lines of 32 or 64 characters, 5-by-7 dot matrix.
Operator input: Keyboard.
Data storage: Phi-Deck tape transport cassette.
Production: Introduced in July of 1977. In production by August of 1977.
Cost: $2770 kit, $3800 assembled.
The 77 had an operating system on EROM.　　　　**Value $100-$150**

H11

Heath Data Systems H11
Processor: DEC LSI-11.
RAM: 4 K expandable to 20 K.　　　　　　　　　　　　(cont.)

Display: Recommended to be used with H9 video terminal. Could display 12 lines of 80 characters each, or 48 lines of 20 characters each.
Operator input: Designed for used with a terminal.
Data storage: Paper tape, cassette or floppy drive.
Physical: Metal case painted and styled to match other Heath peripherals. Had a steel chassis.
Production: Introduced at the Personal Computing show at the end of August 1977 in Atlantic City. Was still on sale by October of 1980.
Cost: $1295 for the kit.   **Value: $125-$175**

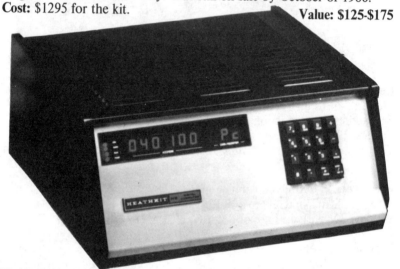

Heath Data Systems H8
Processor: Intel 8080A running at 2.048 MHz.
RAM: 1 K, expandable to 32 K.
Display: 4 status LED lights and 9 7-segment LED displays. A 12-inch CRT display was available.
Operator input: 16-key hexadecimal keyboard, 67-key keyboard optional.
Data storage: Initially paper tape (H10 reader) and 1200 Baud cassette, later the Heath H17 floppy disk system was available.
Physical: 16"W by 17.5"D by 6.5"H, weighed 21 pounds.
Production: Introduced at the Personal Computing show in 1977 in Atlantic City, and was delivered in the fall. Was still advertised in October of 1980.
Cost: $375 for the bare kit, $1500 for the 16 K system with cassette drive and H9 terminal.

This machine was sold as a kit with CPU board fully wired and tested, and a ROM monitor. It was billed as "one of the lowest-cost general-purpose computers on the market," and had a built-in speaker and clock. All software was available at no extra charge, and systems software was available in four fan-fold paper tapes for $20. Benton Harbor

(cont.)

BASIC was available, and manuals were $25. Suggested uses for the machine were as a trainer to learn about microprocessors, an entertainment center, a hobby, education or "home management center" for telephone numbers, budget, checkbook, taxes, inventory. Its 50-line Heath bus could address 65 K bytes.

Value $125-$175

Parasitic Engineering   Equinox 100
Processor: Intel 8080 and 8080A, running at 2 MHz.
RAM: 64 K, 4 K memory kit available for $109.
Display: 10-digit LED octal display.
Operator input: Octal keyboard with 12 keys.
Data storage: Could drive three audio cassette drives and used 300-Baud Kansas City Standard for data transfer.
Physical: 7"H by 17"W by 20"D. Had an aluminum case with a smoked Plexiglass front panel.
Production: Introduced about September of 1977.
Cost: $699 as a kit initially, but increased to $799.

Advertisements for this machine stressed computing with it more than using it. BASIC-EQ and an editor and assembler were available on cassette. It had a carrying handle and a keyed power lock for security, and 20 expansion slots. This machine was produced as a joint venture with Morrow's MicroStuff. A single board was available that supplied both RS-232 and 8-bit parallel.

Value: $100-$150

IMSAI (IMS Associates, Inc.) PCS-80
Processor: Intel 8080, running at 3 MHz.
RAM: 16 K
Display: CRT displaying 24 lines of 80 characters each.
Operator input: Keyboard.
Data storage: Single or dual mini or standard floppy disks were available.
Physical: Housed in a blue metal box.
Production: Was in production by September of 1977.
Cost: $1499 assembled.

This S-100 machine had a serial port. Billed as an "integrated component system," it was made up of IMSAI components to be a complete system that can be configured exactly to the customer's needs. It came with CP/M, BASIC and FORTRAN IV, and its Advertisements were aimed at businessmen, personal users, education and industry.
Value: $75-$150

IMSAI (IMS Associates, Inc.) PCS-80/30
Processor: Intel 8085, running at 3 MHz.
RAM: 2 K, expandable to 64 K.
Display: Black-and-white built-in 5-inch monitor, displaying 12 lines of 40 characters each or 24 lines of 80 characters each.
Operator input: Keyboard.
Data storage: Cassette or 5.25-inch floppy drive.
Production: In production by January of 1978.
Cost: $1349 as a kit, $1499 assembled.

This machine had eight expansion slots and one parallel and two serial ports. Assembler, DOS, BASIC and FORTRAN IV were available.
Value: $75-$150

IMSAI (IMS Associates, Inc.) VDP-80/1000
RAM: 32 K.
Display: 12-inch.
Data storage: Dual floppy drives.
Production: In production by 1978.
Cost: $6000.

This machine had 7 expansion slots and a 28 amp power supply.
Value: $75-$150

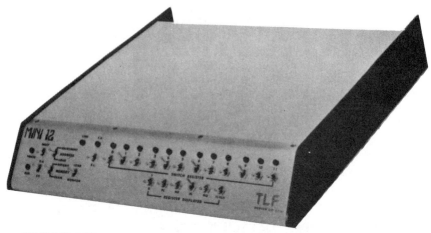

TLF Mini 12
RAM: 8 K, expandable to 32 K.
Data storage: Had a controller for eight digital tape drives.
Production: In production by September of 1977.

This DEC PDP-8E compatible used 12-bit words and came assembled. It had a monitor bootstrap in ROM, and a built in serial interface.
Value: $100-$150

MITS (Micro Instrumentation and Telemetry Systems) Altair Turnkey 8800b
RAM: 1 K.
Display: 5 LEDs.
Operator input: Two toggle switches.
Production: Introduced about October of 1977.

This machine had a very different appearance from the earlier Altairs. It had a nearly-bare front panel, a key-operated power switch, and a serial I/O port. It was basically a version of the 8800b with a single circuit board.
Value: $225-$300

MCS Microcomputer System   TEI Processor Terminal
Processor: Intel 8080.
RAM: 16 K.
Display: 15-inch "high-resolution" black-and-white video "with an optical filter face plate to reduce glare and improve type visibility."
Operator input: Detached keyboard with 8 function keys.
Data storage: Shugart SA-400 mini-floppy disk drive, 90 K capacity and IBM-compatible format.
Physical: "Heavy-duty aluminum cabinet, fan and washable filter. All edge connectors and card guides provided..."
Production: In production by October of 1977.
Cost: $3495 fully assembled and tested, $2995 for partially assembled kit.

This machine came with CP/M and BASIC available on disk. It was similar to the MCS-PT by CMC Marketing Corp.

Value: $75-$150

CMC Marketing MCS-PT112/32
Processor: Intel 8080.
RAM: 16 K, with more optional.
Display: 24-line by 80-character display on a 15-inch high-resolution monitor.
Operator input: Full upper and lower case ASCII keyboard with 8 special function keys and a numeric keypad.
Data storage: One 5.25-inch Shugart SA-400 Minifloppy was standard.
Physical: Had an aluminum cabinet and a cooling fan.
Production: Introduced about January of 1978.
Cost: With disk drive: $2995 as a kit, $3495 assembled. Without disk drive: $2195 as a kit, $2495 assembled.

This machine had a 12-slot mainframe, came with CP/M DOS and BASIC. Three parallel and serial ports were available. It was similar to the TEI Processor by MCS Microcomputer System.

Value: $75-$150

IMSAI (IMS Associates, Inc.) VDP-80
Processor: Intel 8085, running at 3 MHz.
RAM: 32 K, expandable to 196 K.
Display: 12-inch monitor.
Operator input: 62-key keyboard with 12-key numeric and 12-key control keypads.
Data storage: Dual PerSci double-density drives with 1 M byte storage were standard. Three more could be added.
Production: In production by March of 1978.
Cost: $5995.

This machine was unreliable when first introduced and caused the company problems. It had parallel and serial I/O. BASIC and FORTRAN IV were available.

Value: $75-$150

RCA Cosmac Super Elf
RAM: 4 K expansion board kit was available.
Display: Video output supported graphics.
Operator input: Hex keypad.
Data storage: Cassette interface available on expansion board..
Production: In production by April of 1978.
Cost: $106.

The Super Elf was a kit. Parallel and serial ports were available as options, as was an S-100 memory interface.

Value: $75-$125

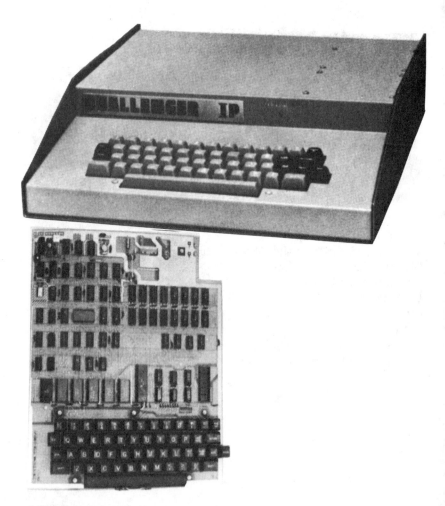

OSI (Ohio Scientific Instruments) Challenger IP
Processor: 6502.
RAM: 4 K, expandable to 32 K.
Display: RF converter for TV, runs at 256-by-256 pixel resolution.
Operator input: 53-keyboard with upper and lower case and user programmability.
Data storage: Kansas City standard audio cassette interface and dual floppy drive interface were available.
Production: In production by May of 1979.
Cost: $349.

The Superboard mainboard was also sold as a single-board system under the name of Superboard II for $279. The IP had graphics capability, 8 K Microsoft BASIC in RAM.

Value: $125-$175

OSI (Ohio Scientific Instruments) Challenger II
RAM: 16 K, expandable to 192 K.
Data storage: 8-inch floppy disk drives were available as a kit or assembled. A 74 Mby hard drive was available.
Production: In production by October of 1977.
Cost: $1964 for complete assembled system.

This machine could simultaneously support as many as four users. It had a serial interface.

Value: $125-$175

OSI (Ohio Scientific Instruments) Challenger IIP
Processor: 6502A, running at 1 or 2 MHz.
RAM: 4 K, expandable to 36 K.
Display: Could drive a 64-character wide video display on a video monitor or TV.
Operator input: Capacitive contact keys.
Data storage: 8-inch floppy disk drives available as a kit or assembled. A cassette interface was available.
Physical: 15" by 15" by 4".
Production: In production by October of 1977.
Cost: $598 assembled.

This machine had BASIC in ROM, and a four-slot backplane for which 15 expansion boards were available.

Value: $125-$175

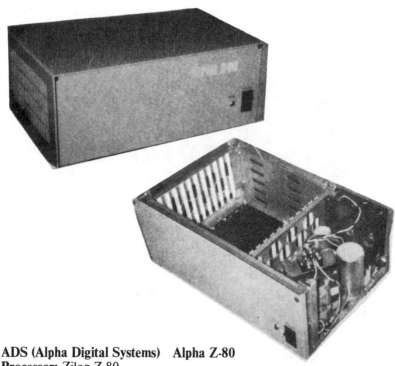

ADS (Alpha Digital Systems) Alpha Z-80
Processor: Zilog Z-80.
Physical: Had a 17 amp power supply, and a cooling fan in the case.
Production: In production in October of 1977.
Cost: $495, $595 with 30-amp power supply and 22 slots.

The Alpha Z-80 had a 12-slot S-100 bus.

Value: $100-$150

OSI (Ohio Scientific Instruments) Model 500
RAM: 4 K.
Physical: 8-by-10-inch board.
Production: In production by October of 1977.
Cost: $298.

This board-only machine had a serial port and used the Ohio Scientific Bus.
Value: $100-$150

Seals Electronics PUP-1
Processor: Zilog Z-80 running at 2.5 MHz, with 4 MHz optional. Other processors were available.
RAM: 32 K standard, expandable to 500 K.
Dual storage: Dual Shugart mini-floppy disk drives with 86 K per disk.
Physical: Came as a free-standing unit, but rack mounting was optional.
Production: Announced about November of 1977.

"PUP" stood for "Peripheral Universal Processor." Included DOS, extended BASIC, and sample business routines. This S-100 machine had 11 expansion slots, and two serial and two parallel communications ports.

Value: $75-$150

Gnat Computers GNAT-PAC System 8
RAM: 16 K.
Display: Hex display on the front panel.
Operator input: Hex input on front panel.
Data storage: Had dual minifloppy disk drives with 80 K bytes storage each.
Production: Introduced about November of 1977.
Cost: $3690

This machine had 2 K bytes of PROM, with space for an additional 14 K. The monitor and loader were PROM resident. PL/M, BASIC, and FOR-TRAN were available.

Value: $75-$150

Andromeda Systems   Model 11/B
Processor: LSI-11.
RAM: 20 K of 16-bit words.
Display: 24 line by 80 characters per line terminal, communicated with the terminal via RS-232 at 9600 bps.
Data storage: A dual floppy drive system offered 512 K of storage.
Production: Introduced about November of 1977.

This turnkey system used the RT-11 operating system and had an RS-232 interface.   **Value: $75-$150**

EPA (Electronic Product Associates) Micro68b
Processor: Motorola 6800.
RAM: 8 K.
Data storage: Had dual or single integrated floppy disk system (compatible with IBM standards). A cassette interface was also included.
Production: Introduced about November of 1977.
Cost: $1878 for the base system. The single disk system was $2595, and the dual floppy system was $3295.

FORTRAN IV and BASIC were available with this machine, as were 20 mA current-loop and RS-232 interfaces.

Value: $75-$150

Computer Power and Light   COMPAL-80
Processor: Intel 8080A.
RAM: 16 K.
Data storage: Cassette or floppy drive.
Production: In production in 1977.
Cost: $2300.

This was an S-100 machine.   **Value: $75-$125**

E and L Instruments MMD-1
Processor: Intel 8080A.
RAM: 500 bytes.
Display: LEDs.
Operator input: Octal entry.
Data storage: Cassette.
Production: In production by 1977.
Cost: $422.50 as a kit, $600 assembled.   **Value: $75-$150**

Electronic Control Tech ECT-100-8080
Processor: Intel 8080A.
Production: In production by 1977.
Cost: $320 as a kit, $500 assembled.

This was an S-100 machine.

Value: $75-$150

Byte 8
Production: In production by 1976.
This machine was sold at BYTE shops.

Value: $300-$500

Olson 8080 Microcomputer
Production: In production by 1976.
This machine was sold at BYTE shops, and was a variant of the Byte.
Value: $250-$450

IMSAI (IMS Associates, Inc.) PCS-80/15
Processor: Intel 8085.
Production: In production by December of 1977.
Cost: $749 as a kit, or $929 assembled.

Value: $75-$150

Vector Graphic Memorite
Processor: Intel 8080A.
Production: In production by January of 1978.

This S-100 machine was available as a turn-key text editor, with typewriter/printer and CRT.

Value: $75-$125

OSI (Ohio Scientific Instruments) Challenger III
Processor: 6502A, Motorola 6800, and Zilog Z-80 processors.
RAM: 32 K.
Data storage: 8-inch floppy disk drives available as a kit or assembled.
Production: Introduced about January of 1978.
Cost: $3481 with 32 K, fully assembled, but no terminal.

This machine had three microprocessors, and ran "all software published in the small computer journals." It had automatic switching between processors, under software control. Ran the OS65D operating system. A serial interface was available.

Value: $100-$150

PolyMorphic Systems 8813
Processor: Intel 8080.
RAM: 16 K.
Display: CRT.
Operator input: Detachable keyboard.
Data storage: Could drive one, two or three minifloppy disks.
Physical: Had a walnut cabinet with a brushed aluminum front panel.
Production: Introduced about January of 1978.
Cost: $3250 with one drive, $3840 with two drives, $4430 with three drives.

This machine was advertised for the professional rather than the hobbyist. Advertising copy claimed "the System 8813 will make you more productive in your profession," and would allow "you to perform complex financial, engineering, and scientific models in the comfort of your office or den." It came with BASIC, and could display graphics.

Value: $100-$200

Cromemco System Three
Processor: Zilog Z-80, running at 4 MHz.
RAM: 32 K (in two 16 K byte cards), expandable to 512 K.
Display: CRT and driver card available for $1595.
Operator input: CRT terminal.
Data storage: Came with two floppy drives, but could drive up to four. Had motor-driven disk loading and unloading, disks could be ejected by software.
Production: Introduced about January of 1978.

The System Three had both an RS-232 interface and a parallel interface. FORTRAN IV, BASIC and Z-80 macroassembler were available on IBM-format, soft-sectored diskettes. Two line-printers were available: 180 CPS for $2995, and 60 CPS for $1495. It had a 21-slot S-100 bus.

Value: $75-$150

Microdata Systems F800
Processor: Mostek F8.
RAM: 8 K, with 4 K memory boards available at $129 as a kit or $199 assembled.
Production: Introduced about January of 1978.
Cost: $499 as a kit, $699 assembled.

This machine had a 12-slot motherboard. A 5 K BASIC interpreter was included. I/O options included RS-232 or 20 mA current-loop.
Value: $75-$125

BPI MicroNOVA
Processor: microNOVA.
RAM: 8 K, expandable to 64 K.
Data storage: 315 K floppy drive.
Production: In production by 1978.

This machine had nine expansion slots and a serial interface.
Value: $75-$125

Micromege Micro M16
Processor: National PACE 16.
RAM: Could accept 4 memory cards with 16 K of 16-bit words each.
Production: In production by January of 1978.

This machine came with an EROM bootloader, low and high speed current loop and RS-232 serial ports, two 1200 bps audio cassette ports, 8 K macroassembler and 8 K PACE BASIC. It had a "gunstock walnut veneer" cabinet.
Value: $75-$125

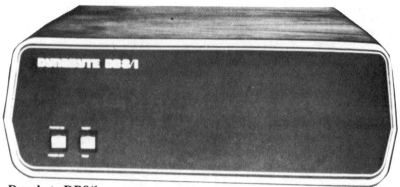

Dynabyte DB8/1
Processor: Zilog Z-80, running at 4 MHz.
RAM: 32 K.
Data storage: Could drive two 8-inch floppy drives (the DB8/4 System).
Physical: Metal construction with lighted indicator switches. Was also available as a rack-mount unit.
Production: In production by October of 1978.

This CP/M system was aimed at the business and professional market. It could be supplied with BASIC, FORTRAN, COBAL and various word-processing and business software. It had a 12-slot backplane, and one parallel and two serial interfaces. **Value: $75-$125**

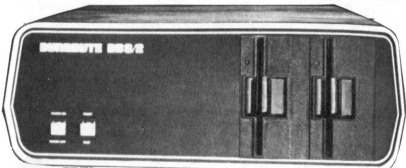

Dynabyte DB8/2
Processor: Zilog Z-80 running at 4 MHz.
RAM: 32 K.
Data storage: Two 5.25-inch (600 K) Micropolis floppy drives.
Physical: Metal construction and lighted indicator switches. Was also available as a rack-mount unit.
Production: In production by January of 1978.

This CP/M system was aimed at the business and professional market. It could be supplied with BASIC, FORTRAN, COBAL and various word-processing and business software. It had a 12-slot backplane, and one parallel and two serial interfaces. **Value: $75-$125**

Digital Systems   Micro-2
Processor: Zilog Z-80.
RAM: 32 K.
Data storage: Dual Shugart drives with either IBM 3740 format or double-density format giving 571 K per floppy drive.
Production: Introduced in February of 1978.
Cost: $4995

This CP/M machine came with BASIC and a real-time clock. CBASIC and FORTRAN were also available. It had up to four RS-232 serial ports and one 16-bit parallel port.

Value: $75-$125

SWTPC (Southwest Technical Products Corp.) 6800/2
Processor: Motorola 6800, running at 2 MHz.
RAM: 4 K, expandable to 32 K.
Display: Monochrome television.
Production: Introduced about February of 1978.
Cost: $439 as a kit, $495 assembled.

The 6800/2 had 8 K of ROM/PROM, and came with a monitor that had a 6820 PIA proprietary bus and its MP-S serial interface which was RS-232 and 20 ma TTy interfaces.

Value: $100-$175

Unicomp SS-11/15
Data storage: Dual floppy drive.
Physical: Available in 10.5-inch rack or tabletop mount.
Production: In production by February of 1978.

This LSI-based system was compatible with DEC software, such as multiuser BASIC, FORTRAN and MACRO-11.

Value: $125-$175

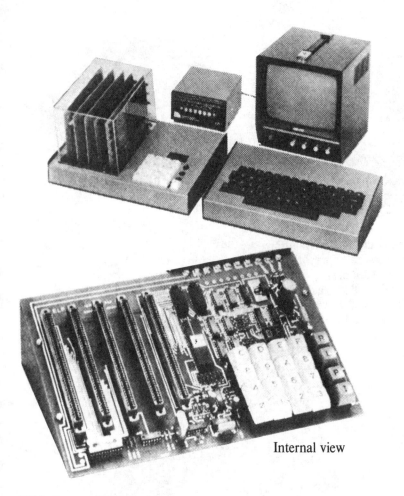

Internal view

RCA Cosmac Elf II
Processor: RCA Cosmac COS/MOS.
RAM: 256 bytes.
Display: Two digit hexadecimal display.
Operator input: Full hexadecimal keyboard.
Data storage: Cassette.
Production: In production by April of 1978.
Cost: $99.95.

This machine had RS-232C and 8-bit TTY I/Os. Tiny BASIC was available.
Value: $75-$125

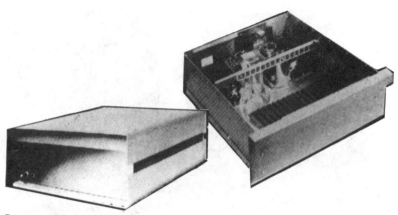

Integrand S-100 Mainframe
Processor: Apparently none, this machine came with just a mainframe (backplane bus).
Physical: Both rack and desk models available.
Production: In production by April of 1978.
Cost: $200 for the rack-mounted model, $235 for the desk model.

This SS-50 machine had 15-slots, a cooling fan and was sold fully assembled.
Value: $75-$125

Bally Professional Arcade
Processor: Zilog Z-80.
RAM: 12 K.
Operator input: 24-key keyboard.
Production: In production by April of 1978.
Cost: $299.95.

Advertised as "the only video game the home user can program," the Arcade came with three games: Gunfight, Checkmate and Scribbling. Tiny BASIC available for $49.95.

Value: $50-$100

OSI (Ohio Scientific Instruments) Challenger C2-8P
Processor: 6502, running at 1 MHz.
RAM: 4 K, expandable to 32 K.
Display: Black-and-white video display interface, that could display 32 lines of 64 characters each in upper and lower case.
Operator input: Keyboard with upper and lower case characters.
Data storage: A cassette recorder was optional (a Panasonic unit was shown in advertisements). It could have 8-inch floppy drives, and was claimed to be "the only personal class computer that can be expanded to support a Hard Disk! (CD-74)."
Production: In production by July of 1978.
Cost: $825.00.

The C2-8P had both RS-232 and parallel interfaces, and 8 K BASIC in ROM. It was billed as "the fastest full feature BASIC in the microcomputer industry." Sold fully assembled and tested, its 8-slot mainframe had six slots available for expansion. **Value: $100-$125**

Technico SS-16
Processor: TMS9900.
RAM: Expandable to 64 K.
Display: 64-color video board was available.
Data storage: Dual floppy or minifloppy.
Production: In production by October of 1978.

The SS-16 could accommodate up to 6 RS-232 and 20 mA current loop interfaces. BASIC was available.

Value: $75-$125

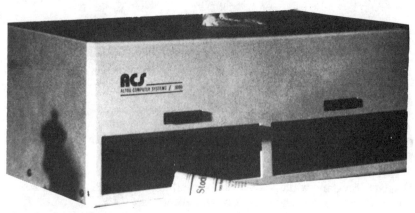

Altos Computer Systems ACS8000
Processor: Zilog Z-80, running at 4 MHz.
RAM: 32 K, expandable to 64 K.
Data storage: Shugart 8-inch IBM compatible floppy drives, with capacities of: 1/2, 1, 2, or 4 M-byte. A hard-disk was available with up to 58 M-byte capacity.
Production: In production by October of 1978.
Cost:$3840, $5990 with dual 8-inch floppy drives.

The ACS8000 was billed as a "true single board computer." It supported CP/M, BASIC, COBAL, PASCAL and FORTRAN IV. Had one serial and two parallel ports.

Value: $75-$125

OSI (Ohio Scientific Instruments) C3-OEM
Processor: Had a triple processor board with 6502A, Motorola 6800, or Intel 8080 or Zilog Z-80.
RAM: 32 K.
Date storage: 500 K in two 8-inch floppy drives.
Production: In production by December of 1978.
Cost: $3590.

Intended as a controller for large equipment, this machine could also run small-systems software. It was available in table or rack mounted configurations, had one RS-232 serial port, and came with 6502 DOS and BASIC, and an 8-slot motherboard of which four were used for the basic machine.
Value: $100-$125

Synertek SYM-1
Processor: SY6502.
RAM: 1 K, expandable to 4 K.
Display: Could be made to drive an oscilloscope.
Operator input: 28-key audio response keypad.
Physical: No case, a single-board computer with keypad attached.
Production: Introduced about December of 1978.
Cost: $269.

This KIM-compatible had 4 K ROM, an RS-232 serial port and a TTY current-loop.
Value: $50-$100

Vector MZ
Processor: Zilog Z-80 running at 4 MHz.
RAM: 32 K, expandable to 64 K.
Data storage: Two Micropolis quad-density floppy drives (315 K per drive).
Production: In production by January of 1979.
Cost: $3750.
This system had 18 expansion ports. It came with one serial and two parallel ports.

Value: $75-$125

JF Products 68
Processor: Motorola 6800.
Data storage: Cassette interface built-in.
Production: In production by January 1979.
Cost: $549.95 as a kit, $749.95 assembled.

This machine was based on the SS-50 bus and had 16 expansion slots. It had a woodgrain cabinet, and a 9600-Baud serial port. **Value: $75-$125**

Rockwell AIM-65
RAM: 1 K and 4 K models were available.
Display: Built-in thermal printer.
Operator input: Built-in keyboard.
Production: In production by April of 1979.
Cost: $375 for the 1 K machine, $450 for the 2 K machine. Was available as a special package with 4 K assembler/editor in ROM, 8 K BASIC in ROM, power supply and case for $599.

An unusual feature of this KIM-1 compatible was its on-board printer.
Value: $125-$175

Technical Design Labs ZPU
Processor: Zilog Z-80.
Production: In production by 1979.
Cost: $269 kit, $325 assembled.

Value: $75-$125

Martin Research   Mike 8
Processor: Zilog Z-80.
Display: 6 coded LED digits.
Operator input: Calculator-style keyboard.
Production: Introduced in 1979.
Cost: $495

Value: $50-$100

Courtesy of Quay Corporation

Quay 80 AI
Processor: Zilog Z-80, running at 2.5 MHz.
RAM: 8 K.
Data storage: Cassette.
Production: In production from November of 1976 to about 1979.
Several hundred were made.
Cost: $450 a kit, $600 assembled.

The 80AI was an S-100 bus machine. It was part of the Quay 800 microcom-puter system.

Value: $75-$125

ibs (independent business systems) Betasystem
Processor: "Multiple independent Z-80 processors for up to 10 users,"
running at 4 MHz.
RAM: 64 K per processor card, for a total of 400 K.
Data storage: Two to 4 Micropolis 5.25-inch floppy drives gave storage
of 1.2 M. An 11 to 40 M 8-inch hard drive was available.
Physical: The Betasystem II was housed in a "furniture quality
cabinet."
Production: In production by April 1979.
Cost: Floppy-drive systems were priced from $4695.

This machine was based on the North Star, and had a full-screen text editor
and Pascal and BASIC compilers. It was marketed as a system, including
a printer and monitor.

Value: $100-$150

SWTPC (Southwest Technical Products Corp.) MC-6809
Processor: Motorola 6809.
Production: In production by May of 1979.
Cost: $1500.

The MP-09 processor card alone was sold for $195.

Value: $100-$150

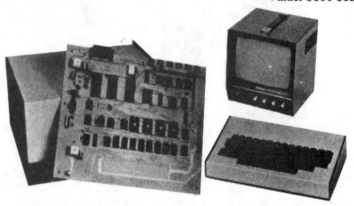

Netronics R&D Ltd Explorer/85
Processor: Intel 8085.
Data storage: Could drive a cassette.
Production: In production by June of 1979.
Cost: Prices start at $129.95, but rose with features.

This was a kit that could be expanded by levels. It had an S-100 bus with six expansion slots.

Value: $50-$100

MicroDaSys MD-690a
Processor: Motorola 6809.
RAM: 1 K.
Data storage: 2400-Baud cassette interface.
Physical: A single-board computer in the Kim mold.
Production: In production by June of 1979.
Cost: $239 as a kit, $299 assembled.

This single-board S-100 computer came with a real-time clock.

Value: $50-$100

Hitachi   TDS-IB
Data storage: Floppy drive with 87.5 K per disk. Could drive up to four drives.
Production: In production by July of 1979.

This very early Japanese machine was offered through Trade of Industrial Products (TIP) from Japan. It came with TDOS (TIP DOS).

Value: $175-$250

AMSAT-GOLEM-80
Processor: Intel 8080 or Zilog Z-80.
Production: In production by September of 1979.

This was a prototype kit computer, designed to be built in stages as a project for experimenters. It used the S-100 bus.

Value: $100-$150

Ithaca InterSystems DPA-1
Processor: Zilog Z-80 running at 4 MHz.
Production: Introduced fall of 1979.

This system had an S-100 bus with twenty expansion slots. Pascal was available.

Value: $100-$150

Digital Sport Systems   Informer 3
Processor: Zilog Z-80.
RAM: 48 K.
Display: CRT with 24-line by 80-character display.
Data storage: 8-inch floppy drive.
Production: In production by December of 1979.
Cost: Less than $4000.

This machine came with two RS-232 ports and one parallel port, diagnostics, BASIC and file and disk-copying capabilities.

Value: $75-$125

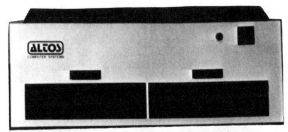

Disk drive
unit

Altos Computer Systems   Sun-Series ACS8000-6
Processor: Zilog Z-80.
RAM: Expandable up to 208 K.
Data storage: Two Shugart 8-inch floppy drives and 14.5 M Shugart
hard drive.
Production: In production by December of 1979.
Cost: Under $9500.

For $12,000 this machine came with four-user CP/M. It could be equipped
with up to six serial and two parallel ports. BASIC, FORTRAN, COBOL,
Pascal, APL, C and various business applications were available.
Value: $75-$125

Altos Computer Systems   ACS8000-5
Processor: Zilog Z-80A.
Production: Introduced in 1980.
Cost: About $8500

This multi-user system could support four users.
Value: $75-$125

OSI (Ohio Scientific Instruments) Challenger C4P
Processor: 6502.
RAM: 8 K, expandable to 32 K.
Display: The optional color monitor displayed 32 lines of 64 characters each, with a resolution of 256 by 512 pixels.
Operator input: 53-key keyboard.
Data storage: Both cassette and mini-floppies (two) were options.
Cost: 8 K unit was $649.
Production: Was in production by October of 1979.

This machine had one expansion slot, BASIC in ROM, and keypad and joystick interfaces.

Value: $100-$125

OSI (Ohio Scientific Instruments) Challenger C4P MF
Processor: 6502A.
RAM: 24 K, expandable to 48 K.
Display: RF modulator was available to drive a home TV, displaying 32 lines of 64 characters each, and having a resolution of 356-by-512 pixels. Color graphics were available.
Operator input: 53-key keyboard, and could drive joysticks and keypad.
Data storage: Could drive a cassette, but came with a 5.25-inch floppy drive. It could drive two floppy drives.
Cost: $1695.
Production: Was in production by October of 1979.

The C4P MF had a programmable tone generator that could generate tones from 200 to 20 KHz, and had a real-time clock and two RS-232 ports. Its main language was MicroSoft BASIC, which was stored on disk. A home security system was available, driven through two special 16-line parallel interfaces.

Value: $100-$125

OSI (Ohio Scientific Instruments) Challenger C8P
Processor: 6502.
RAM: 8 K, expandable to 32 K.
Display: A color TV monitor was available as an accessory with 32 lines of 64 characters.
Operator input: 53-key keyboard. Also has keypad and joystick interfaces.
Data storage: Cassette and dual 8-inch floppy drive were available. Could drive a Winchester disk.
Production: In production by October of 1979.

This machine had BASIC in ROM. Advertisements claimed software could be easily adapted from TRS-80 Level II, Apple II floating point BASIC and Commodore BASIC, and stated "The C8P is an 8-slot mainframe class computer with five open slots. It features over 3 times the expansion capability of the C4P for advanced home, experimental and small business applications."

Value: $100-$125

Action Computer Enterprise Discovery MP Series A
Processor: Up to four Intel 8080s.
RAM: 32 K expandable to 64 K.
Display: CRT with 24 lines by 80 columns.
Data storage: Two 8-inch floppy drives.
Production: In production by January of 1980.
Cost: Prices ranged from $3000 for a single-user system up to $11,000 for a four-user system.

This system was available in one to four-user configurations, and was also available in kit form. There were two serial and two parallel ports per processor. It used S-100 bus. Ran CP/M, and came with CBASIC-II.

Value: $100-$150

Cromemco Z-2D
Processor: Zilog Z-80.
Display: Could interface to CRT through an RS-232 serial port.
Data storage: Standard with 5.25-inch floppy drive (92 K), optional with two floppy drives, could handle four.
Production: In production by January of 1980.
Cost: With 1 floppy drive the kit was $1495, or $2095 assembled. Additional floppy drive was $495.

The Z-2D was available with a FORTRAN IV compiler, 16 K disk BASIC, and Z-80 assembler ($95 each). It had a 21-slot S-100 bus.

Value: $75-$150

Cromemco Z-2H
Processor: Zilog Z-80A, running at 4 MHz.
RAM: 64 K.
Data storage: Two floppy-disk drives and an 11 M hard-drive.
Production: In production by November of 1979.

Value: $75-$150

95

RCA Cosmac VIP-711
Processor: CDP1802, running at 1.76 MHz.
RAM: 2 K, expandable to 32 K.
Display: Black-and-white or color TV.
Operator input: 16-key hexadecimal keypad. 58-key membrane keyboard optional.
Data storage: Cassette.
Production: In production by 1980.
Cost: $249

This machine had a parallel interface and a 22-pin proprietary bus.
Value: $50-$125

OSI (Ohio Scientific Instruments) C8P DF
RAM: 32 K.
Display: 32 lines of 64 characters each, with a resolution of 256-by-512 pixels. Could display up to 16 colors.
Operator input: 53-key ASCII keyboard.
Data storage: Two 8-inch floppy drives. The C8P was available with a cassette interface instead of the floppies.
Production: In production by March of 1980.
Cost: The C8P was $895, and the C8P DF was $2597.

This was OSI's top-of-the-line personal computer, and it was claimed that "the standard model is twice as fast as other personal computers such as the Apple II and PET." It was "available with a GT option which nearly doubles the speed again, making it comparable to high end mini-computer systems." The system came with a real-time clock and 8-expansion ports.
Value: $100-$125

PerCom Data Company SBC/9
Processor: Motorola 6809.
Production: In production by March of 1980.

The SBC/9 used SS-50 bus.   **Value: $75-$125**

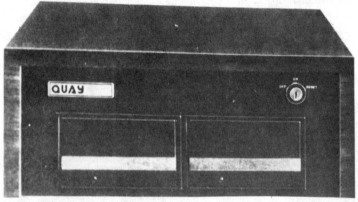

Quay 500 Series (500 and 520)
Processor: Zilog Z-80, running at 4 MHz.
RAM: 64 K.
Data storage: The 500 came standard with two 200 K floppy drives,
but could be expanded to four. The 520 came with quad-density drives
(400 K each).
Production: In production by December of 1980.
Cost: The 500 was $2992 and the 520 was $3495.

This single-board computer ran CP/M.   **Value: $75-$150**

Quay 900 Series
Processor: Zilog Z-80, running at 4 MHz.
RAM: 48 K, expandable to 65 K.
Data storage: Dual quad-density 8-inch floppy drives (2.5 M byte),
could be expanded up to 5 M byte, IBM 3740 format compatible.
Production: In production by May of 1980.
Cost: Under $4000.

*This was a single-board computer running CP/M. It came with an
assembler, editor and debugger. It had an RS-232 or TTY serial port, and
parallel port (Centronics-compatible). An S-100 bus adaptor was available
for expansion.*   **Value: $75-$150**

97

Morrow Designs Decision 1
Processor: Zilog Z-80.
Data storage: Could support two 800 K floppy drive or two 2.1 M
8-inch floppy drives and a 26 M hard drive.
Production: In production by December of 1980.

This multi-tasking system was designed for business use and word-processing. It had a UNIX-compatible operating system, and would also run CP/M.
Value: $75-$150

Quasar Data Products QDP-100
Processor: Zilog Z-80, running at 4 MHz.
RAM: 64 K.
Display: CRT in a terminal.
Operator input: Keyboard and numeric keypad in a terminal.
Data storage: Two 8-inch double-sided, double-density floppy drives.
Production: In production by June of 1980.
Cost: $4695.

An S-100 machine running CP/M 2.2. It included BASIC, a PROM burner, a real-time clock, two serial and two parallel ports. It could be upgraded to become a QDP-8100.
Value: $75-$150

Quasar Data Products QDP-8100
Processor: Zilog Z-8000, running at 4 MHz.
RAM: 64 K.
Display: CRT in a terminal.
Operator input: Keyboard and numeric keypad in a terminal.
Data storage: Two 8-inch double-sided, double-density floppy drives.
Production: In production by May of 1980.

An S-100 machine running CP/M 2.2, the QDP-8100 included BASIC and a Z-80 emulator. It had two serial and two parallel ports.
Value: $75-$150

North Star   Advantage
Processor: Zilog Z-80A.
RAM: 64 K.
Display: Black-and-white monitor.
Operator input: 87-key keyboard with 15 programmable function keys.
Data storage: Two built-in 360 K 5.25-inch floppy drives.
Production: Introduced in 1981.
Cost: $3595.

The Advantage was a single-board computer. It ran CP/M or DOS operating systems.
Value: $50-$100

OSI (Ohio Scientific Instruments) Challenger C1P
Processor: 6502.
RAM: 8 K, expandable to 32 K.
Display: Black-and-white, 24 lines of 24 characters, or 12 lines of 48 characters.
Operator input: 53-key keyboard.
Data storage: Cassette.
Production: In production by 1982.
Value: $75-$125

OSI (Ohio Scientific Instruments) Challenger C1P MF
RAM: 20 K, expandable to 32 K.
Display: Color.
Operator input: 53-key keyboard.
Data storage: Floppy drive.
Production: In production by 1982.

Value: $75-$125

OSI (Ohio Scientific Instruments) Challenger C4P DF
RAM: 48 K, expandable to 96 K.
Display: Color monitor with 32 lines of 64 characters each. Displayed upper and clower case.
Operator input: 53-key keyboard.
Data storage: 8-inch floppy drive.
Production: Was in production by 1982.

Value: $75-$125

OSI (Ohio Scientific Instruments) Challenger C8P DF
Processor: 6502A.
RAM: 32 K, expandable to 48 K.
Display: A color TV monitor was an accessory. It displayed 32 lines of 64 characters each, and had a resolution of 256-by-512 pixels.
Operator input: 53-key keyboard, and keypad and joystick interfaces.
Data storage: Dual 8-inch floppy drives standard, Winchester drive optional.
Production: In production by 1982.

The C8P DF had BASIC on disk, and a real-time clock.

Value: $75-$125

Quasar Data Products QDP-300F1H10
Processor: Zilog Z-80B, running at 6 MHz.
RAM: 192 K.
Data storage: 1.2 M double-sided double-density 8-inch floppy drive, and 10 M or 15 M hard drive.
Physical: 19.5" by 18" by 8.25", weighed 50 pounds.
Production: In production by 1984.
Cost: $6395 with hard drive and 192 K, $3995 with 128 K and extra floppy instead of the hard drive.

This machine ran version 2.2 of the CP/M-80 operating system. It had two S-100 expansion slots, 2 RS-232C serial ports, and 2 parallel ports.

Value: $50-$75

II-2. CONSUMER, OR "APPLIANCE" MACHINES

In 1977 development of the personal computer took a major step forward with the introduction of three machines with the integrated appearance of today's personal computers. The Apple II, Radio Shack TRS-80, and Commodore PET, with their conventional qwerty keyboard input and CRT displays, were marketable to a much wider range of consumer than the early generation of machines. The rate of sales of personal computers again increased. While the market still remained relatively specialized, with many machines used for programming in BASIC, the rather limited selection of software was growing fast, and making personal computers useful to non-programmers.

The next milestone in the development of the personal computer would come in 1981, when the IBM PC would give the standardization needed for another surge of market growth.

IBM (International Business Machines) 5100
RAM: 16, 32, 48 or 64 K.
Display: Built-in video screen displaying 16 lines of 64 characters per line. A television monitor output was available as an option.
Operator input: Built-in keyboard with separate numeric keypad.
Data storage: Built-in tape drives held 204 K characters. Optional 5106 auxilary tape drive was available for $2300.
Physical: Weighed 50 pounds and was about the size of a briefcase.
Production: Announced September 9, 1975.
Cost: Ranged from $8975 to $19,975, depending on RAM and language.

While the 5100 was perhaps too costly to be considered a personal computer, it nonetheless was IBM's first entry into the market and thus was a significant machine. It was not the direct predecessor of the 5150 PC. APL and BASIC were available in ROM. The 5103 132-column, 80 cps dot-matrix printer was available as an option for $3675.
Value: $300-$500

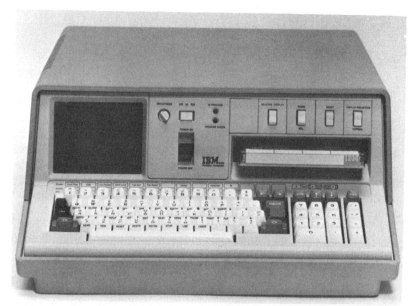

IBM 5100, Courtesy of International Business Machines Corporation

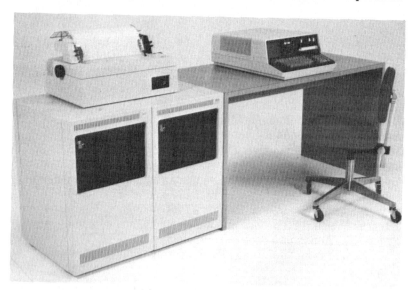

IBM 5100 computing system, Courtesy of International Business Machines Corporation

TI (Texas Instruments) Model 990/4
Processor: TI TMS 9900.
RAM: 512 K in the basic configuration. 16 K in the development-system and prototyping-system configurations. Expandable to 58 K.
Physical: It was available as a "low-cost OEM package," a desktop configuration, and a 13-slot rack-mount.
Production: Introduced about October of 1975, along with the TMS 9900 microprocessor and Model 990/10 minicomputer.
Cost: $368 with 512 bytes, $512 with 8 K. $1216 with a power supply, 6-slot mainframe, 8 K, and a "programmer's panel".

This early microcomputer had a single circuit board.

Value: $100-$200

Apple II
Processor: 6502 running at 1 MHz.
RAM: 4 K, expandable to 64 K.
Display: The Apple II could drive a color or black-and-white TV with a resolution of 24 lines of 40 characters per line. It initially displayed only a 40-character lower case set, but later went to 80-character upper and lower case.
Operator input: Integral 52-key keyboard.
Data storage: Initially cassettes were used. A 5.25-inch floppy disk was introduced at the March 1978 Second West Coast Computer Faire, and began shipping in June of 1978. The floppy disk and controller were available for $585.
Physical: 18" by 15.25" by 4.5", weighed 12 pounds.
Cost: $1295 initially, but dropped to $970 about two years later (with 2 K, it was $1795 with 48 K). The board alone was available for $598. A few years later the pricing was $975 for the 16 K machine, $1059 for the 32 K machine and $1123 for the 48 K machine.
Production: A working prototype was in existence by August of 1976. The machine was introduced in April 1977 at the West Coast Computer Faire in San Fransisco, and became available in Summer of 1977. Production was doubling very three to four months by the end

of the year. By September 1979 yearly sales were over 35,000, which was over four times the sales of the previous year.

This machine was instrumental in greatly expanding the personal-computer market. It had an 8-slot motherboard. Advertising was aimed at the home market, and some copy read: "Clear the kitchen table. Bring in the color TV. Plug in your new Apple II, and connect any standard cassette recorder/player." "Only Apple II makes it that easy. It's a complete, ready to use computer, not a kit." "It's the first personal computer with a fast version of BASIC permanently stored in ROM."

Value: $100-$200

An early Commodore, labeled PET.

CBM 2001.

Commodore PET 2001
Processor: 6502, running at 1 MHz.
RAM: 4 K, expandable to 32 K.
Display: Built-in 9-inch video monitor with 64 standard upper-case ASCII and graphics characters (accessed by shifting). By 1980, when the CBM designation came out, 80 columns of upper and lower-case characters could be displayed.
Operator input: 73-key keyboard with calculator-style keys and a numeric keypad. By 1980, when the CBM designation came out, the keyboard was expanded and improved.
Data storage: Built-in cassette, and 5.25-inch floppy drives were available.
Physical: 16.5"W by 18.5" D by 14"H, weighed 44 pounds.
Cost: $595 with 4 K RAM, $795 with 8 K.
Production: Introduced in June of 1977.

This early appliance computer was offered by Commodore Business Machines, a maker of hand-held calculators. It had 14 K of ROM containing a 4 K operating system and 8 K MicroSoft BASIC. Serial and parallel ports were available for $100 to $175. A very important machine in that it, along with the Apple II and TRS-80, introduced the "appliance computer" era. The name was changed from "PET" to "CBM" for Commodore Business Machine in 1980.

104

Value: $75-$125

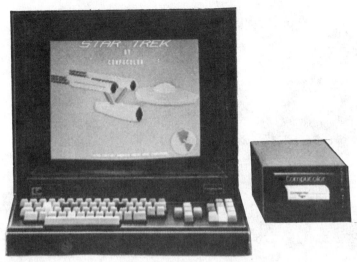

ISC (Intelligent Systems Corp.) Compucolor 8001
Processor: Intel 8080 or 8080A.
RAM: 16 K, expandable to 64 K.
Display: 160-by-192 pixels in color.
Data storage: Came with "Floppy Tape Memory," an 8-track continuous loop tape system that could hold 1024 K bytes per tape. A mini disk drive was an option.
Production: In production by mid-1977.
Cost: $2750.

The 8001 came with an 11 K ROM containing the system and BASIC.
Value: $50-$100

Digital Group System I
Processor: Zilog Z-80.
RAM: 10 K.
Display: 9-inch display of 16 lines of 64 characters each.
Operator input: 76-key keyboard with numeric keypad.
Data storage: Cassette.
Cost: $895 as a kit, $1295 assembled.
Production: In production by 1977.

Value: $50-$75

HP (Hewlett-Packard) 9831A
Display: 32-character LED alphanumeric.
Operator input: Keyboard.
Data storage: An on-board tape drive held 250 bytes, and had an average access time of six-seconds.
Production: Introduced about July of 1977.
Cost: $7200

Value: $50-$100

Tandy/Radio Shack TRS-80 Model I
Processor: Zilog Z-80.
RAM: 16 K, expandable to 64 K.
Display: 12-inch black-and-white monitor, displaying 1024 characters in 16 lines of 64 characters each.
Operator input: 53-key keyboard.
Data storage: Cassette.
Physical: The Model 1 had a hinged door on the back to allow access to I/O connector. The keyboard unit (containing microprocessor and memory) was 16.5" by 8" by 3.5".
Cost: Keyboard and processor only was $399.95.
Production: Announced August 3, 1977, and 10,000 were sold by September.

Advertised using the "appliance" theme. One advertisement showed a couple using the machine in their kitchen, similar to the Apple II advertisements, with the copy: "for people who want to use a computer now - without the delay, work and problems of building one." It was billed as useful for personal finances, accounting, teaching, kitchen computations and games. BASIC was stored in ROM.

Value: $75-$100

Scientific Research Firmware System
Processor: Intel 8080 or Zilog Z-80.
RAM: 65 K.
Display: Video terminal.
Operator input: Keyboard on video terminal.
Data storage: Floppy disk with over 600 K byte capacity.
Cost: $8999
Production: In production by September of 1977.

This S-100 machine offered an integrated package of hardware and soft-
ware aimed at the business market. Advertisements claimed "No switches
to set, Power-on operation." It came with a line printer, extended BASIC,
and numerous application software programs, including ledger, payroll,
word processing, medical engineering, statistics and more, including help
and tutorial programs. A claim was that it "includes over $25,000 of
business programs." It had multiple I/O ports.

Value: $50-$75

Noval 760
Processor: Intel 8080A.
RAM: 16 K.
Display: 12-inch monochrome video monitor.
Operator input: Keyboard.
Data storage: PhiDeck cassette
Physical: Housed in a desk that folded up to look like furniture.
Production: In production by September of 1977.

The 760 was aimed at the advanced hobbyist who wanted to develop pro-
grams. It was an assembled unit, and had 3 K of PROM system software.
It came with a printer.

Value: $50-$100

Digital Electronics Corp DE68DT
RAM: Could be expanded to 65 K.
Display: 20-character alphanumeric display.
Operator input: Keyboard.
Data storage: One 5.25-inch floppy drive.
Production: Introduced about January of 1978.
Cost: Prices started at $2200.

This machine had a 40 character/line impact printer built in and a nine-
slot card cage. A 6 K byte operating and debugging system was available
as an option in ROM. Software also included BASIC and FORTRAN.

Value: $50-75

A.O. Smith Mesa Two
RAM: 64 K.
Display: CRT.
Operator input: Keyboard.
Data storage: 10 Mbytes.
Production: Introduced about January of 1978.

Intended as a small business computer, the Mesa Two came with business software including accounts, payroll, general ledger, etc. It was meant to be operated "without the need for data processing technicians," and came with a printer.

Value: $50-$75

iCOM Microperipherals Attache
Processor: Intel 8080.
RAM: 1 K to 16 K.
Display: Display of 16 lines of 64 characters per line outputted through video jack.
Operator input: Full ASCII keyboard was integrated in the case.
Production: In production by March of 1978.
Cost: $1449.

This S-100 machine had 10 expansion slots. iCOM and MITS (the maker of the Altair) were part of Pertec Computer Corporation's Microcomputer division when this machine was produced. It was offered ready-to-use, and was specifically aimed at the appliance computer market.

Value: $50-$75

TI (Texas Instruments) SR60A
Display: Alphanumeric display and 20-character alphanumeric printer.
Data storage: Could drive up to two cassettes.
Production: Introduced about March of 1978.
Cost: Prices started at $1995.

Referred to as a "personal computer/calculator" by TI, the SR60A was aimed at the business market. It had up to 2640 program steps or 330 data registers, but this could be expanded to 7920 program steps and 990 data registers. Serial communications were available.

Value: $50-$75

Northwest Microcomputer Systems 85/P
Processor: Intel 8085A, running at 3 MHz. Five MHz operation was optionally available.
RAM: 54 K of 450 ns static RAM.
Display: Integral 12-inch CRT displayed 24 lines of 80 characters each.
Operator input: Built-in Hall-effect, 103-key keyboard.
Data storage: Two double-density Shugart floppy drives gave 1 M of storage.
Production: Was in production by May of 1978.
Cost: $7495

This turnkey unit came with PASCAL, two serial ports, and offered a "choice of solid oak or walnut cabinet."

Value: $50-$75

Compucolor 8051
Display: Color monitor with 48 lines of 80 characters each.
Operator input: Extended ASCII keyboard.
Data storage: Early models used cassettes, later models used floppy drive systems.
Production: In production by May of 1978.

A principle claim of the advertisements for this machine was its color monitor.

Value: $50-$100

Exidy Sorcerer
Processor: Zilog Z-80
RAM: 8 K, expandable to 32 K.
Display: Could drive a video display at 30 lines of 64 characters per line, or 512 by 240 pixels.
Operator input: 79-key keyboard with numeric keypad and function keys.
Data storage: Cassette or two floppy drives. A 10 M Winchester hard disk drive was also available.
Physical: 19.25" by 13" by 4".
Cost: $895
Production: Introduced in 1978.

The Sorcerer had "pre-packaged" programs on cassette tapes. Plug-in ROM cartridges had BASIC, Assembler and editor, and a word-processor. It had serial and parallel ports built in, and a 6-slot S-100 expansion unit was optional. It was related to the PSC PS-80.

Value: $25-$50

Mostek Corp. AID-80F
Processor: Zilog Z-80.
RAM: 16 K.
Data storage: Could drive up to four drives with soft-sector format.
Production: In production by June of 1978.
Cost: $5995.

This machine had four 8-bit I/O ports.

Value: $50-75

IBM (International Business Machines) 5110
Display: 16 lines of 64 characters per line.
Operator input: Built-in keyboard.
Production: In production by July of 1978.

Billed at the March 1978 West Coast Computer Show as a system for personal, business and scientific computing. This machine was the successor to the 5100. It used the APL programming language.

Value: $125-$200

Terminal module

SWTPC (Southwest Technical Products Corp.) System B
RAM: 40 K.
Display: CRT in terminal module.
Operator input: Keyboard in terminal module.
Data storage: Two floppy drives gave 1.2 M of storage.
Production: In production by August of 1978.
Cost: $4495.

This machine came installed in a desk with a laminated woodgrained plastic surface.

Value: $50-$75

Infinite UC2000
Processor: Intel 8080.
Display: 12-inch CRT.
Production: Was in production by September of 1978.
Cost: Prices started at $995

This 8-slot S-100 based machine was available in five different configurations (B through E) ranging from empty mainframe to full computer with printer and a cooling fan. It had DB25 connectors on the rear.

Value: $75-$125

Digital Sport Systems Sirius II
Processor: Mostek Z-80 for main computations and a Fairchild 3870 for keyboard and video interface.
RAM: 32 K.
Display: Video interface.
Operator input: 64-key keyboard.
Production: In production by September of 1978.
Cost: $1850
This machine had an RS-232 interface. It came with BASIC and other software for business and games on disk. **Value: $50-$75**

Zentec Corp. ZMS-70
RAM: Up to 64 K.
Display: Integral 15-inch diagonal CRT.
Operator input: Integral keyboard.
Data storage: 143 K of floppy drive storage.
Production: In production by September of 1978.
Cost: Less than $5000
A printer interface and printer were available. Much software was included with the machine. **Value: $50-$75**

TANO Outpost II
Processor: M6800.
RAM: 32 K.
Display: Integral CRT displaying 24 lines of 80 characters each. Characters were found in a 7-by-9 dot matrix.
Operator input: Integral ASCII keyboard.
Data storage: Shugart mini-floppy drives.
Production: In production by September of 1978.
Cost: $1995 plus $35 freight and insurance.

The Outpost 11 came with a BASIC software package, and was advertised as "a ruggedly designed unit, intended for heavy use." It was aimed at the business market. **Value: $75-$100**

IMSAI (IMS Associates, Inc.) VDP-40
Processor: Intel 8085.
RAM: 32 K, could be expanded up to 1/2 M using 64 K RAM boards.
Display: Had a built-in 9-inch CRT, displaying 24 lines of 80 characters each.
Operator input: Integral keyboard.
Data storage: Two floppy drives. Could be expanded to up to 5 M storage.
Physical: Had a "handsome flip-top cabinet for easy access."
Production: In production by September of 1978.
Cost: $4207 by credit card or $4046 by cash.

Described as "a fully integrated video data processor in a single cabinet,"
this S-100 machine had open expansion slots, serial and parallel I/O ports.
It came assembled and tested, and was advertised for small business use.
Value: $75-$100

Compucolor II
Processor: Intel 8080A running at 2 MHz.
RAM: 4 K, expandable to 16 K.
Display: 13-inch 8-color monitor, with 16 lines of 64 characters.
Operator input: Keyboard.
Data storage: Built-in 51 K 5.25-inch floppy drive, later 75 K.
Physical: Had a woodgrained case.
Cost: Ranged from $795 to $1995.
Production: In production by October of 1978.

This machine was available in five models, and software included games, programs for checkbook balancing and tax compilation. It had a 50-pin proprietary bus.

Value: $50-$100

Compucolor Model III
Cost: $1395.
Production: In production by 1978.
Value: $50-$75

Reston Recomp-I
Processor: RCA 1802.
RAM: 8 K.
Display: RF modulator to drive a TV interface. Had full color graphics capability.
Operator input: Both ASCII and hex keyboards built in.
Data storage: Tape-recorder interface.
Physical: Came in "a handsome, functional plastic case."
Physical: In production by October of 1978.

The Recomp-I had a 3-amp power supply, and came with BASIC, machine language and Assembly built in. It was sold as a kit.

Value: $50-$75

Unretouched Photograph of Screen

ISC (Intelligent Systems Corp) Intercolor 8070, Series 1
Processor: Intel 8080A.
RAM: 16 K, expandable.
Display: Eight-color 19-inch display.
Operator input: Integrated keyboard.
Data storage: Dual 8-inch floppy drives (591 K bytes).
Production: In production by October of 1978.
Cost: $6999.99.

This system was aimed at small business, and came with a 110 CPS printer, BASIC, payroll programs and manuals.

Value: $50-$75

MicroDaSys
Processor: Motorola 6809.
RAM: 1 K or 8 K.
Display: Could drive a TV. Displayed 16 lines of 64-characters each in both upper and lower case.
Data storage: 2400-Baud cassette interface.
Production: In production by late 1978.
Cost: $549 with 1 K, $699 with 8 K on a 32 K RAM card.

This updated version of the 690a was aimed more at the "appliance" computer market than the earlier version. It was an S-100 kit machine with an RS-232 interface and 8 K BASIC in PROM.

Value: $50-$75

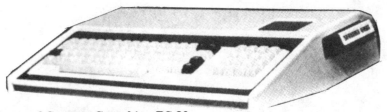

Personal Systems Consulting PS-80
Processor: Zilog Z-80.
RAM: 8 K, expandable to 32 K.
Display: Drives a monitor at a resolution of 240 by 512 pixels or 30 lines of 64 characters each.
Operator input: Integral 79-key keyboard with 16-key numeric keypad.
Production: In production by late 1978.
Cost: $895 for the 8 K version, $1150 for the 16 K version, and $1395 for the 32 K version.

The PS-80 had external PROM cartridges, and came standard with a MicroSoft BASIC cartridge. It had an RS-232 port, a parallel port, and dual cassette recorder ports that ran at 300 or 1200 Baud. An S-100 expansion box was available. It was related to the Exidy Sorcerer.

Value: $25-$50

Tandy/Radio Shack   TRS-80 Level-II
RAM: 16 K, could add up to 48 K.
Operator input: Had a full-size typewriter keyboard. A numeric keypad was new for 1979.
Data storage: Could drive from 1 to 4 mini-disks, or dual cassette recorders.
Production: In production by January of 1979.
Cost: $988.

RS-232C was available, as was much software, including games and business applications.

Value: $50-$75

Interact
Processor: Intel 8080.
RAM: 16 K.
Display: Could drive a color TV through its antenna terminal, and transmit sound through the TV.
Operator input: 9-inch, 53-key keyboard.
Physical: 19"L by 12"W by 8"D, 12 pounds.
Production: In production by April of 1979. Out of production by about February of 1983. Perhaps about 50,000 were made.
Cost: $588.00.

This machine was aimed at business, music, home and education use. It came with BASIC, and was advertised as portable.

Value: $25-$50

TRS-80 Model II, Courtesy of Tandy Corporation

Tandy/Radio Shack TRS-80 Model II
Processor: Zilog Z-80.
RAM: 32 K, expandable to 64 K.
Display: 12-inch black-and-white monitor displaying 24 lines of 80 characters each. Displayed upper and lower case characters.
Operator input: 76-key keyboard with numeric keypad and function keys.
Data storage: Built-in 8-inch floppy drive, but extra floppy drives and a hard drive were available.
Cost: $3499 with 64 K and one floppy drive.
Production: Announced on May 30, 1979.

Billed as "a state-of-the-art business machine," it had one parallel and two serial ports.

Value: $50-$75

apf Electronics   The Imagination Machine
Processor: Motorola 6800.
RAM: 9 K.
Display: A built-in RF modulator drove an 8-color display with a resolution of 128-by-192 pixels, or a 4-color display of 256-by-192 pixels.
Operator input: 53-key "typewriter" keyboard, and two built-in joysticks with numeric keypads.
Data storage: Built-in dual-track cassette loaded at 1500 Baud. "System II" included a 72 K mini-floppy
Production: Was in production by May of 1979.
Cost: "System II," with mini-floppy and 8 K RAM memory cartridge was $995.

This machine had color and sound, and 14 K BASIC in ROM.
Value: $25-$50

Intertec Data Systems   SuperBrain Video Computer System
Processor: Two Zilog Z-80 processors running at 4 MHz. One was for processor- and screen-related functions, the other handled disk I/O.
RAM: 32 K, expandable to 64 K.
Display: 12-inch display of 25 lines of 80 characters per line.
Operator input: Built-in keyboard with numeric keypad.
Data storage: 256 K total storage on two double-density 5.25-inch floppy drives. An optional 10-300 hard drive could be attached through the S-100 bus.
Physical: Was housed in a structural-foam cabinet. Weight was about 45 pounds, and dimensions were: 14 5/8"H by 21 3/8"W by 23 1/8"D. Had a two-board modular design.
Cost: $2685 with 32 K, $2883 with 64 K.
Production: Was introduced in 1979.

This machine had CP/M, a text-editor, assembler and debugger. Advertisements stressed business applications. This single-board design had an RS-232 port and an S-100 adaptor.

Value: $50-$75

Orange
Production: Introduced at the West Coast Computer Faire in 1979.

The Orange was possibly the first Apple clone.

Value: $75-$100

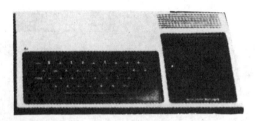

TI (Texas Instruments) 99/4
Processor: TI TMS 9900.
RAM: 16 K, expandable to 72 K.
Display: Came with a 13-inch color monitor that displayed 24 lines of 32 characters each in upper case only.
Operator input: 40-key keyboard.
Data storage: Cassette, or 5.25-inch floppy drive. Also used "Solid State Software command Modules."
Physical: 10.2" by 15.0" by 2.5", weighed less than 5 pounds.
Cost: Initially about $1000, fell to about $100 near the end of production.
Production: Introduced about June of 1979, and was discontinued in 1980.

This machine had an RS-232 interface, BASIC in ROM, and an optional speech synthesizer.

Value: $75-$100

Apple II +
Processor: 6502.
RAM: 16 K, expandable to 64 K.
Display: TV or monitor displaying 24 lines of 40 characters per line.
Operator input: Integral keyboard.
Data storage: Floppy drives.
Costs: $1195 with 48 K.
Production: Introduced in June of 1979.

This machine ran the APPLESOFT system software.

Value: $100-$200

Marinchip Systems M9900 System-1
Processor: TI 9900.
RAM: 60 K.
Display: 24 lines of 80 characters per line.
Operator input: Integral keyboard and numeric keypad.
Data storage: Two 8-inch diskettes. A "40 Megabyte removable car-
tridge disk system" was available for $14,000.
Production: In production by June of 1979.
Cost: $7500. Manual only was $40.

*This S-100 machine came with a network operating system, commercial
BASIC, PASCAL, a word processor, and business applications. Advertisements claimed "If you already have applications in BASIC, you'll be
glad to know that the M9900's BASIC is similar enough to the most popular
8 bit BASIC that conversion won't be a chore." A 165 CPS line printer was
available for $2500.*

Value: $50-$100

NEECO (New England Electronics Co.) Minimax I and II
Processor: 6502, running at 2 MHz.
RAM: 108 K.

(cont.)

123

Display: 12-inch CRT with 240-by-512 pixel resolution.
Operator input: Full keyboard with repeat and numeric keypad.
Data storage: Dual density floppy drive, 5.25-inch (Minimax I) or 8-inch (Minimax II), gave storage of 800 K and 2.4 M respectively.
Production: In production by July of 1979.
Cost: $4495 for Minimax I, $5995 for Minimax II.

Advertised as a "Fully integrated computer system," it had BASIC in 16 K of ROM, and an RS-232C interface.

Value: $50-$100

Heath Data Systems H89 and WH89 "All-In-One Computer"
Processor: Two Zilog Z-80s.
RAM: 16 K, expandable to 48 K.
Display: Built-in CRT.
Operator input: Built-in "professional" keyboard.
Data storage: Built-in 5.25 inch floppy drive with 102 K storage. Could be expanded with the H77 external dual-floppy drive so "You can mount operating system and program disks at the same time, to make computing even faster."
Production: In production by August of 1979.
Cost: $1595.

The H89 ran programs in Microsoft BASIC and Assembler, as well as all H8 software. It was available as a kit or assembled. The WH89 was the same as the H89, but it was assembled.

Value: $75-$100

apf Electronics PeCos One
Processor: 6502.
RAM: 16 K.
Display: Black-and-white, displaying upper case only.
Operator input: Keyboard.
Data storage: Two built-in cassettes.
Physical: 18.5" by 19.5" by 18.5".
Production: In production by 1979.
Cost: About $1600

PeCos stood for Personal Computing System.   **Value: $25-$50**

Umtech VideoBrain
Processor: F8.
RAM: 1 K to 4 K.
Display: Could drive a color TV and display 7 lines of 16 characters
each, as well as operate its speaker.
Operator input: External 36-key keyboard.
Data storage: Cartridge pacs, or cassette.
Production: In production early in 1978.
Cost: $500.

*The VideoBrain came with many programs on plug-in cartridges. It was
to be sold through specialty electronic stores and department stores, and
used ROM cassettes.*   **Value: $75-$175**

Atari 400
Processor: 6502B running at 1.8 MHz.
RAM: 8 K, expandable to 16 K.
Display: Could drive a black-and-white or color television.
Operator input: Membrane keyboard with 57 keys and 4 function keys.
Data storage: Cassette or 5.25-inch floppy drive.
Cost: $549.99.
Production: Introduced in 1978, but did not ship until late in 1979.

*The 400 included a game paddle and joystick as standard. It took ROM
cartridges, and had sound capabilities.*
          Value: $25-$50

Atari 800
Processor: 6502.
RAM: 8 K, expandable to 48 K.
Display: Could drive a black-and-white or color television.
Operator input: Full keyboard.
Data storage: Cassette or 5.25-inch floppy drive. Could access up to 4 floppy drives.
Cost: $999.99 with recorder.
Production: Introduced in 1978, but did not ship until late in 1979.

The 800 had ROM cartridges, a high-speed serial I/O port, and custom sound and graphics chips.

Value: $25-$50

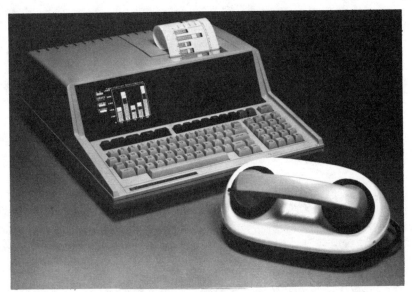

Photo Courtesy of Hewlett-Packard Company

HP (Hewlett-Packard) 85

Processor: Proprietary 8-bit HP processor.

RAM: 16 K, expandable to 32 K.

Display: Built in 5-inch CRT with 256-by-192 pixel resolution, displaying 16 lines of 32 characters each, with 5-by-7 pixel dot matrix characters. Had graphics capability.

Operator input: 92-key keyboard with numeric keypad and function keys.

Data storage: Integral HP DC-100 data cartridge drive with 200 K. Optional 5.25-inch and 8-inch floppy disks available.

Physical: 16" by 18" by 6", weighed just under 20 pounds.

Production: Introduced in January of 1980. HP-85A available about November 1980.

Cost: $3250 was initial list price, but it was available then for as low as $2899. Later was available for as low as $2500.

The HP-85 was the first of the Series 80 family from HP. It had a built-in thermal printer, four I/O ports and HP BASIC in ROM. Math and science software was available. However, it only used HP peripherals and software and this proprietary aspect of it hurt sales. A high-quality machine with nicely integrated design.

Value: $100-$150

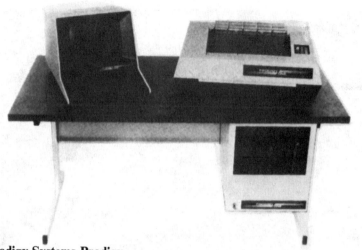

Prodigy Systems Prodigy
Production: In production by January of 1980.

The Prodigy used PROTEGE, Prodigy's "small business applications development language," and was aimed at the business market.

Value: $50-$75

Zenith Data Systems Z-89 Computer System
RAM: 16 K, expandable to 48 K.
Display: Integral, Z-19 display.
Operator input: Built-in keyboard with numeric keypad.
Data storage: Built-in 5.25-inch floppy disk, available with dual floppy disk.
Production: In production by February 1980.
Cost: 16 K unit was $2295, 48 K unit was $2595.

This first Zenith computer was often advertised as a "Zenith-Heath," as it was basically the same machine as the H89. It had two serial ports, and ran CP/M.

Value: $75-$100

ISC (Intelligent Systems Corp) Intercolor 8963
RAM: 32 K.
Display: Built-in color display.
Data storage: 591 K in dual 8-inch floppy drives.
Production: In production by March of 1980.
Cost: $6395.

The 8963 used the CP/M2 operating system. It came with Microsoft Business BASIC.

Value: $50-$75

Vector System B
RAM: 64 K.
Display: Vector Mindless Terminal.
Operator input: Vector Mindless Terminal.
Data storage: Dual floppy drives gave 630 K of storage.
Production: In production by March of 1980.

The System B came with Digital Research 2.0 CP/M, Microsoft BASIC, business software, and a printer.

Value: $50-$75

Electrolabs Pragmatix 100
Processor: Zilog Z-80, running at 4 MHz.
Display: Terminal displaying 80 lines of 24 characters each.
Operator input: Keyboard with numeric keypad on terminal.
Data storage: Two 8-inch floppy drive with a single/double density controller. A double-sided floppy drive was optional. 10 and 20 M removable hard drives were available.
Production: Was in production by March of 1980.
Cost: $6995 assembled and tested.

Advertisements for this S-100 machine claimed "complete computer package...practical to operate...designed for the businessman/woman (even for non-computer specialists)." It came with a 132-column dot matrix printer and compiler business Basic. Its OS-1 operating system ran any CP/M or Cromemco program. An Osborne business software package was available, as was operation with 220 V/50 Hz power.

Value: $50-$75

Chrislin Industries CI-103
Processor: DEC LSI 11/2 or LSI 11/23.
RAM: 256 K.
Display: VT-100 or VT-103.
Operator input: Complete keyboard with numeric keypad.
Data storage: 10 M cartridge disk system was available with a controller. It was compatible to the RT11, and cost $6100.
Production: In production by March of 1980.
Cost: $9600 with LSI 11/23 and 256 K, $4500 with LSI 11/2 and 64 K, $6750 with LSI 11/23 and 96 K.

Advertised as a "Complete system totally enclosed within VT100 Video Terminal."

Value: $50-$75

Mattel Intellivision
Procesor: 16-bit.
RAM: 16 K, expandable to 8 M.
Display: Could drive a black-and-white or color television.
Operator input: 60-key keyboard with numeric keypad. It came with two hand-held controllers.
Data storage: Built-in cassette.
Cost: $550.
Production: Introduced about May of 1980.

Had two parallel ports and plug-in ROM cartridges. This machine was also sold by Atari.

Value: $20-$40

Commodore 8000 Series
RAM: 16 K in the 8016, 32 K in the 8032.
Display: Built-in CRT with 2000-character display (25 80-column lines). Could display 64 ASCII and 64 graphic characters in a 2-by-8 pixel dot matrix.
Operator input: 73-key keyboard.
Data storage: Had two cassette ports. CBM 8050 dual floppy drives were available for $1695, to give 974 K of storage. The 2040 floppy drive was also available for $1295.
Production: In production by May of 1980.
Cost: The 8016 was $1495. The 8032 was $1795.

Billed as a "business computer," the 8000 Series had both parallel and IEEE-488 interfaces.

Value: $25-$50

Sinclair Research ZX80
Processor: Zilog Z-80A running at 3.25 MHz.
RAM: 1 K, expandable to 16 K.
Display: Black-and-white or color TV, displaying 24 lines of 32 characters each.
Operator input: 40-key integral membrane keyboard.
Data storage: Cassette.
Physical: 6.5" by 8.5" by 1.5", weighed 12 ounces.
Cost: $199.95
Production: The ZX80 was initially marketed in the UK in 1980, and tens of thousands of units were sold in Europe by the end of that year.

Billed as "the world's first truly portable computer," it still required AC power and a TV. It came with 4 K integer BASIC, and floating-point basic available on an 8 K chip. It was the first microcomputer to sell for under $200.

Value: $15-$30

TI (Texas Instruments) 99/4A
Production: Introduced in August of 1980, and was discontinued in
October of 1983.
Cost: Sold for $299 when TI offered a $100 rebate on Aug. 6, 1982.
Final price in late 1983 was $49.95.

The TI-99/4A was an improved version of the TI-99/4.

Value: $50-$100

Apple III
Processor: 6502A running at 1.4 MHz.
RAM: 96 K, expandable first to 128 K, later to 256 K.
Display: 12-inch monitor displaying 24 lines of 40 or 80 characters per
line of upper and lower case characters.
Operator input: Keyboard with numeric keypad.
Data storage: Built-in 5.25-inch floppy drive.
Cost: Initially prices started at $3495, but later these dropped to near
$3000. Could cost up to about $8000 with options.
Production: The Apple III was introduced at the National Computer
Conference in September 1980, and shipments started that fall. It was
re-introduced in late fall 1981 with more memory and a hard disk
drive.

*The early Apple IIIs were plagued with reliability problems, and the model
ultimately was unsuccessful. These machines had four expansion slots and
two serial ports.*

Value: $75-$125

Commodore VIC-20 (Video Interface Computer)
Processor: 6502A.
RAM: 8 K, expandable to 32 K.
Display: Color TV displaying upper and lower case characters in 22 lines of 23 characters each.
Operator input: Keyboard with four programmable function keys.
Data storage: Cassette, 5.25-inch floppy drive, or cartridge.
Cost: $299
Production: Introduced in 1980, and was still selling strong in 1982 when the popular Commodore 64 was introduced.

Joysticks and game-paddles were available for this popular machine. It was designed to be sold with little support from the outlet, and to be very easy to use. It had one serial port.

Value: $20-$40

Courtesy of International Business Machines Corporation

IBM (International Business Machines) 5120
Display: Built-in CRT.
Operator input: Numeric keypad.
Data storage: Two built-in 8-inch floppy drives. It could have 1.2 M or 2.4 M storage capacity.
Production: Announced in March of 1980.

The 5120 had BASIC and APL in ROM. This machine was the successor to the 5100, and was based on the 5110 Model 3. **Value: $100-$175**

134

Oki Electric BMC if800 Model 20
Display: CRT.
Operator input: Separate keyboard unit.
Data storage: Microcassette and two minifloppy drives of 280 K capacity each. An Oki 10 M hard drive was optional.
Production: Introduced in June of 1980.

This machine came with a printer.

Value: $75-$100

Oki Electric BMC if800 Model 30
Data storage: Two 8-inch floppy drives mounted vertically. An Oki 10 M hard drive was optional.
Production: Introduced in June of 1980.

The Model 30 came with a better printer than was included with the Model 20.

Value: $75-$100

NEC (Nippon Electric Co.) PC-8000
Processor: NEC µ PD-780C-1.
RAM: 16 K, expandable to 32 K.
Display: TV
Operator input: 82-key keyboard.
Data storage: Cassette, or the PC-8031 floppy disk. Up to four floppy disks could be attached.
Physical: The CPU was housed in the keyboard unit, which was called the PC-8001. The PC-8012A was an expansion chassis that contained 7 expansion slots, a 2 K PROM, and 32 K of additional RAM.
Production: Introduced in 1980.

The PC-8000 system, part of the PC-6000 and PC-8800 family of computers sold in Japan, was one of the first Japanese machines to sell in volume in the U.S. It ran N-BASIC.

Value: $75-$100

Personal Micro Computers PMC-80
Processor: Zilog Z-80.
RAM: 16 K, expandable to 48 K.
Display: TV.
Operator input: 10 function keys.
Data storage: Had a built-in cassette, but could adapt to 5.25-inch disks.
Cost: $645 for the 16 K model.
Production: Was in production by October of 1980.

This machine was a clone of the TRS-80 Model 1. Had an optional S-100 expansion unit.

Value: $50-$75

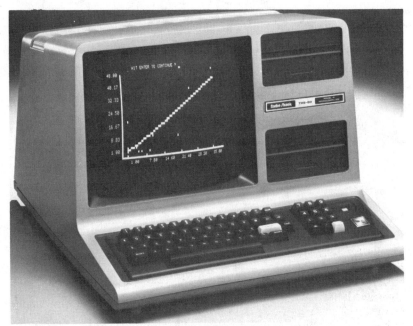

Courtesy of Tandy Corporation

Tandy/Radio Shack TRS-80 Model III
Processor: Zilog Z-80
RAM: 4 K, 16 K, 32 K or 48 K.
Display: Black-and-white 12-inch monitor, displaying 16 lines of 64 upper-case characters each, or 16 lines of 32 upper and lower case characters each.
Operator input: 65-key keyboard with 12-key numeric keypad.
Data storage: Cassette or 5.25-inch floppy disk. Could support up to four 5.25-inch floppy disks of 175 K each.
Physical: An advertisement stated the Model III was "housed in a one-piece molded case sporting the familiar battleship-gray motif." The one-piece construction was to meet FCC requirements.
Cost: $630 for the basic Level I 4 K system, up to $999 for the 16 K version with Model III BASIC.
Production: Introduced about October 1980.

Later on in production hard drives were available from several manufacturers. A serial port was available as a $100 option. Much software was written for this popular computer, and in this respect it was perhaps second only to the Apple II.

Value: $30-$50

Tandy/Radio Shack TRS-80 Color Computer
Processor: Motorola 6899E.

Courtesy of Tandy
Corporation

RAM: 4 K, expandable to 16 K.
Display: Has a built-in TV modulator, 8 colors, displaying 16 lines of
32 characters each, graphics resolution was 128-by-192 pixels. TV was
not included, but Radio Shack offered a 13-inch color TV for $399.
Operator input: Integral 53-key keyboard, joysticks available.
Data storage: Used plug-in ROM packs, and could drive a cassette
recorder (which was not included).
Physical: A plastic case with integral keyboard.
Production: Introduced about October of 1980.
Cost: Prices ranged from $360 with 4 K to $540 with 16 K.

Value: $30-$50

MicroAce
Processor: Zilog Z-80.
RAM: 1 K, expandable to 2 K.
Display: TV driver displayed 24 lines of 32 characters each, and sup-
ported graphics.
Operator input: Membrane keyboard.
Data storage: Could drive a cassette recorder.
Production: In production by late 1980.
Cost: $149 with 1 K, $169 with 2 K.

This kit came with a BASIC interpreter in ROM.

Value: $10-$25

NEC (Nippon Electric Co.) PC-6000
Processor: NEC μ PD-780C-1.
RAM: 16 K to 64 K.
Display: Could drive a monitor.
Operator input: Integral keyboard.
Production: Introduced late in 1981.

The PC-6000 had BASIC in ROM. It was an inexpensive machine sold mainly in Japan. It could use ROM packs and Atari joysticks.
Value: $75-$125

Casio FX-9000P
Processor: Intel 8080A
RAM: 8 K.
Display: Built-in 5-inch display, displaying 16 lines of 32 characters each.
Data storage: Cassette.
Cost: Under $900.
Production: Introduced about November 1980.

This was Casio's first computer. It had instantaneous operation on power-up and graphics capabilities, and used CMOS low-power RAM packs that could be removed. They were priced at $189 for a 4 K pack.
Value: $25-$50

Cromemco System Zero/D
RAM: 64 K.
Production: Introduced about November 1980.
Cost: The Zero listed at $995, but was available for about $850. The Zero/D had a list price at introduction of $2995, but was available for $2545.

The Zero/D was also available in a plain "Zero" version with less features.
Value: $50-$100

Sinclair Research ZX81
RAM: 1 K.
Operator input: Membrane keyboard.
Production: Production began in March of 1981.
Cost: Near the end of its production the price fell to below $100.

This successor to the ZX80 was sold by Timex.
Value: $15-$30

Xerox 820
Processor: Zilog Z-80.
Production: Introduced in July of 1981.

The 820 ran CP/M, two versions of BASIC, and used Ethernet. It was sold through ComputerLand.

Value: $75-$100

Timex/Sinclair 1000
RAM: 2 K.
Display: Could drive a CRT.
Data storage: A cassette interface was available.
Production: Originated in February of 1982, when the Sinclair ZX81 was slightly modified and renamed the Timex/Sinclair 1000. It was Announced on April 20, 1982.
Cost: The 1000 initially sold for $99, and was the first computer offered in the United States for less than $100.

The 1000 contained BASIC in ROM.

Value: $15-$30

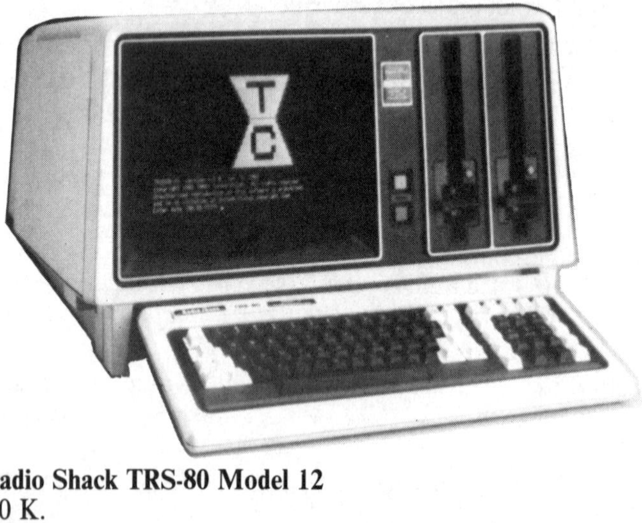

Tandy/Radio Shack TRS-80 Model 12
RAM: 80 K.
Display: 12-inch monitor.
Operator input: Keyboard with numeric keypad.
Data storage: Two 8-inch floppy drives, mounted vertically, each with a 1.25 M storage capacity.
Production: Introduced around 1982.
Cost: $3999 with two floppy disks.

Value: $50-$100

Eagle II
Processor: Zilog Z-80.
RAM: 64 K.
Data storage: Two 360 K 5.25-inch floppy drives.
Production: Introduced about May of 1982.
Cost: $2995.

This machine ran the CP/M operating system.   **Value: $50-$150**

DEC (Digital Equipment Corp.) DECmate II
Processor: 6120 or optional Zilog Z-80A.
RAM: 96 K, expandable to 160 K.
Display: 12-inch black-and-white or 13-inch color.
Operator input: 103-key keyboard with a numeric keypad and 16 pro-
grammable function keys.
Data storage: 267 K 5.25-inch or 128 K 8-inch floppy drives. 5 M or
10 M Winchester drives were optional.
Physical: 19.75" by 14.625" by 6.5"
Production: Announced in Spring of 1982.
Cost: $3745 base price.

This machine was compatible with the PDP-8 minicomputer. It ran the
WPS-8 and COS 310 operating systems, but could also run the CP/M
operating system with Z-80 processor. It had 3 expansion slots, and 2 serial
ports.   **Value: $75-$125**

Commodore 64
Processor: 6510, which was basically a modified 6502.
RAM: 64 K.
Data storage: Floppy drives were available.
Production: Introduced in 1982.
Cost: Initially sold for $595, prices eventually dropped to about $200.

This popular machine came with color graphics and sound capability. It
had a serial interface, and 20 K of ROM containing MicroSoft BASIC. It
was a good machine to run games on, and had a built-in music synthesizer.
Value: $25-$75

Franklin Computer Corp. Ace 100
Production: Announced in 1982.

The Ace 100 was a clone of the popular Apple II.

Value: $50-$75

Z-110 with monitor on top and Z-120 integral monitor,
Courtesy of Zenith Data Systems

Zenith Data Systems Z-110 and Z-120
Processor: Intel 8085 and 8088, both running at 5 MHz.
RAM: 128 K, expandable to 768 K.
Display: Black-and-white or color, displaying 25 lines of 80 characters each.
Operator input: 95-key keyboard with numeric keypad and 13 programmable function keys.
Data storage: Two internal 5.25-inch 320 K floppy drives. External 8-inch floppy drives were available. An 11 M Winchester drive could replace one of the internal floppy drives.
Physical: 19.5" by 19" by 7.5".
Production: Production began late in 1982 and ended early in 1986.
Cost: $2199 as a kit with 192 K and one drive, $3499 with 128 K, two drives and color, $5599 with 192 K, a Winchester drive and black-and-white monitor.

The Z-110 and Z-120 were Zenith's Z-100 series. The Z-110 was a "low profile" model without an integral monitor. The Z-120 had an integral monitor. They ran the CP/M-85 and Z-DOS operating systems, and had five S-100 expansion slots, two RS-232C serial ports, and one parallel port.
Value: $50-$100

Franklin Computer Corp. Ace 1000
RAM: 64 K.
Display: 40 characters per line.
Operator input: Numeric keypad.
Production: In production by 1983.

The Ace 1000 was an Apple II compatible.

Value: $50-$75

Apple IIe
Processor: 6502R, running at 1 MHz.
RAM: 64 K, expandable to 128 K.
Display: Black-and-white or color monitor, displaying 24 lines of 40 or 80 character each. Displayed upper and lower case characters.
Operator input: 64-key keyboard.
Data storage: Cassette or 5.25-inch floppy drive.
Physical: 15.2"W by 18"D by 4.5"H.
Cost: $1395 for main unit only, $1995 with monitor and floppy drive. The later updated version sold for $829 when it came out in 1987.
Production: Introduced in January of 1983. An updated version came out in January of 1987.

The "e" stood for "enhanced." This machine had 7 expansion slots. The IIe line was extended early in 1984 with the addition of a portable version. In late 1983 a mouse was made available for the IIe for about $150.

Value: $125-$250

HP (Hewlett-Packard) 86

RAM: 64 K, expandable to 576 K.
Display: Nine and 12-inch external monitors were available.
Data storage: Could drive two external floppy drives.
Production: Introduced in late 1982.

The HP-86 was a later version of the Series 80 family, of which the HP-85 was the first. It came with BASIC, and was the lower-cost member of the Series 80 family.

Value: $50-$125

Tandy/Radio Shack TRS-80 Model 16

Processor: Motorola 68000 and Zilog Z-80.
RAM: 128 K, expandable to 512 K.
Display: A green video displaying 24 lines of 80 characters each.
Operator input: Keyboard with numeric keypad and function keys.
Data storage: Integral 8-inch floppy drive, but one additional floppy drive and up to four hard drives could be added.
Production: Introduced in 1982.
Cost: $4999

This machine could operate in a multiuser mode. Up to two terminals could be added at $650 each. It had one parallel and two serial ports.

Value: $30-$50

Tandy/Radio Shack TRS-80 Model 16B

Processor: Motorola 68000, running at 6 MHz, and Zilog Z-80A, running at 4 MHz.
RAM: 64 K for the Z-80A. 256 K, expandable to 768 K, for the 68000.
Display: Black-and-white monitor displaying 24 lines of 80 characters each. Could display both upper and lower case.
Operator input: 86-key keyboard with numeric keypad and 8 function keys.
Data storage: 8-inch double-sided double-density 1.25 M floppy drive. 12 M hard drive was available.
Physical: 14" by 21.25" by 23.5", weighed approximately 50 pounds.
Cost: $4999 for 256 K and one floppy drive, $5798 for 256 K and two floppy drives, $9995 for 384 K and one floppy and one hard drive.
Production: Introduced in 1982.

This machine ran the TRSDOS-11/16, TRSDOS-12, and TRS-Xenix operating systems. It had 7 expansion slots, and 3 were free in the 512 K system with a hard drive. There were two RS-232C serial ports, and one parallel port.

Value: $30-$50

HP (Hewlett-Packard) 87XM
RAM: 128 K, expandable to 640 K.
Display: Integral CRT displaying 24 lines of 80 characters each, or 400 by 240 pixels.
Data storage: Could drive external floppy drives.
Production: Introduced in late 1982.

The HP-87XM was a later version of the Series 80 family, of which the HP-85 was the first. It came with BASIC, and was the top of the Series 80 family.

Value: $50-$125

Coleco Adam
Processor: Zilog Z-80.
Production: Introduced in 1983, discontinued in 1985.

This CP/M machine was not popular.

Value: $25-$50

Xerox 820-II
Processor: Zilog Z-80A.
RAM: 64 K.
Display: Black-and-white displaying 24 lines of 80 characters each.
Operator input: Keyboard with numeric keypad.
Data storage: 5.25-inch floppy drive, 8-inch floppy drive, or hard drive.
Production: In production by 1983.
Cost: $2245

This machine ran the CP/M operating system.

Value: $50-$75

Atari 1200XL
Production: Introduced in 1983.

Value: $15-$30

Mattel Aquarius
Production: Introduced in 1983.

Value: $15-$30

DEC (Digital Equipment Corp.) Rainbow 100
Processor: Zilog Z-80A, running at 4.102 MHz, and Intel 8088, running at 4.815 MHz.
RAM: 64 K, expandable to 256 K.
Display: 12-inch black-and-white or 13-inch color monitor displaying 24 lines of 80 characters each or 24 lines of 132 characters each.
Operator input: 103-key keyboard with function keys and LED status lights.
Data storage: Dual or single 400 K 5.25-inch floppy drives and 5 or 10 M Winchester drives.
Physical: 19.25" by 14.3" by 6.5", weighed 30 pounds.
Production: Introduced in 1983. Production ended in 1985.
Cost: $3495 base price.

This machine ran the CP/M, CP/M86, and MS-DOS operating systems. It had two serial ports, and three expansion slots. It's standard VT100 terminal emulation allowed it to serve as a DEC minicomputer terminal.
Value: $50-$75

DEC (Digital Equipment Corp.) Rainbow 100 +
Processor: Both Zilog Z-80A and Intel 8088.
RAM: 128 K, expandable to 896 K.
Display: 12-inch black-and-white or 13-inch color.
Operator input: 103-key keyboard with numeric keypad and 16 function keys.
Data storage: 800 K 5.25-inch floppy drive, and 10 M Winchester drive.
Physical: 19.25" by 14.625" by 6.5".
Production: Introduced in September of 1983. Production ended in 1985.

This machine ran version 2.0 of the CP/M-86/80 operating system. It had 3 expansion slots.
Value: $50-$75

Escort
Display: Built-in 9-inch monitor
Data storage: Two built-in 3.5-inch 322 K floppy drives.
Production: In production by 1983.
Cost: $3995

This machine ran the CP/M operating system.
Value: $50-$75

TeleVideo 802
Processor: Zilog Z-80A
RAM: 64 K.
Display: Black-and-white monitor displaying 24 lines of 80 characters each.
Operator input: Keyboard with numeric keypad and 22 programmable function keys.
Data storage: Two 340 K 5.25-inch floppy drives.
Production: In production by 1983.
Cost: $3495.

This machine ran the CP/M operating system.   **Value: $50-$75**

Sanyo MBC-1000
RAM: 64 K.
Display: Built-in black-and-white 12-inch monitor displaying 25 lines of 80 character each.
Operator input: Keyboard with numeric keypad and 5 function keys.
Data storage: Built-in 326 K floppy drive.
Production: In production by 1983.
Cost: $1795.

This machine ran the CP/M operating system.   **Value: $50-$75**

Morrow Designs Micro Decision
Processor: Zilog Z-80A.
RAM: 64 K.
Display: Black-and-white 12-inch monitor displaying 25 lines of 80 characters each.
Operator input: Keyboard with numeric keypad and 7 programmable function keys.
Production: In production by 1983.
Cost: $1790.
This machine ran the CP/M operating system.   **Value: $50-$75**

ACT (Applied Computer Technologies) Apricot
Processor: Intel 8086.
RAM: 256 K, expandable to 768 K.
Display: 9-inch display. A two-line LCD was included to serve many purposes, including acting as a clock/calendar, as a label for the function keys, and as a calculator display.
Operator input: Keyboard.
Data storage: Two 3.5-inch floppy drives.
Physical: Keyboard and CPU weighed less than 17 pounds, and the monitor weighed about 9 pounds, but could be carried separately.
Production: Introduced in November of 1983.
Cost: $3190.

The Apricot ran version 2.0 of the MS-DOS operating system. A mouse was optional for this British-made machine.   **Value: $50-$75**

Sinclair Research QL
Processor: Motorola 68008.
RAM: 128 K.
Production: Announced in January of 1984.
Cost: $499.

Value: $20-$40

Hitachi MB6890
Processor: Motorola 6809.
RAM: 64 K.
Display: Could drive a color monitor.
Production: In production by 1984.

This machine was sold as "The Peach" in Australia. A light-pen interface was standard with the MB6890, but the pen was not included.

Value: $50-$75

Sharp MZ-2000
Processor: Zilog Z-80A, running at 4 MHz.
RAM: 64 K.
Display: Monochrome monitor.
Operator input: Keyboard with 10 function keys and a numeric keypad.
Data storage: Cassette.
Production: In production by 1984.

Value: $50-$75

Cannon CX-1
Processor: Motorola 6809.
Display: Monochrome monitor, no graphics capabilities.
Data storage: Two 320 K minifloppy disks. Could drive up to four.
Production: In production by 1984.

The CX-1 was aimed at the business market. It had provisions for a light pen.

Value: $50-$75

Apple IIc
Processor: 65C02, running at 1 MHz.
RAM: 128 K.
Display: Black-and-white 9-inch monitor displaying 24 lines of 80 characters each.
Operator input: 64-key keyboard.
Data storage: 5.25-inch floppy drive.
Physical: 11.5"W by 12"D by 2.25"H, weighed 7.5 pounds.
Production: Introduced in April of 1984. An enhanced version was introduced in September of 1986.
Cost: $1295

Billed as a portable, this machine ran the ProDOS operating system. It had two RS-232C serial ports, an external disk port, and a video expansion port.
Value: $200-$400

Tandy/Radio Shack   TRS-80 Model 4
RAM: 16 K, expandable to 64 K.
Display: Integral CRT displayed 16 64-character lines.
Operator input: Integral keyboard.
Data storage: Two integral floppy drives.
Production: In production by 1984.
Cost: $995 with no disks, $1699 with one floppy drive, and $1999 with two floppy disk drives and an RS-232 port.
Value: $50-$75

AGAT
Production: Introduced in November of 1984.
The AGAT was a Soviet version of the Apple II.
Value: $100-$150

Systems Formulate Corporation Bubcom
Processor: Zilog Z-80.
RAM: 64 K.
Display: Bubcom RGB monitor with 160 by 100 or 640 by 200 pixel resolution. Sold for $1400.
Operator input: Keyboard.
Data storage: Eight-inch double-density, double-sided floppy drive was available. It had a capacity of 1.2 M. Also, bubble-memory cartridges were available at $175 each.
Production: In production by 1984.

Value: $75-$125

Photo Courtesy of Hewlett-Packard Company

HP (Hewlett Packard) 86B
Processor: 8-bit HP Processor
RAM: 128 K, expandable to 640 K.
Operator input: Keyboard.
Production: In production by 1985.

The 86B had four expansion slots, and an IEEE-488 interface.
Value: $50-$125

HP (Hewlett-Packard) 226
Processor: Motorola 68000.
RAM: 64 K (initially).
Display: 7-inch monitor displaying 25 lines of 50 character each.
Operator input: Keyboard.
Data storage: Integral 264 K floppy drive.
Production: In production by 1985.

This was the first Series 200 computer. It was designed for science and engineering use.

Value: $50-$125

AT&T Unix PC
Processor: Motorola 68010.
Production: Introduced in 1985.
Cost: $5600.

Value: $75-$100

Atari 520ST
Production: Announced in 1985.

Value: $15-$30

Apple IIGS
Production: Introduced on September 15, 1986.
Cost: $999

Value: $600-$1000

Apple IIc Plus
Production: Introduced in September of 1988.
Cost: $1099 for the color system.

Value: $200-$400

II-3. IBM PC, XT, AND CLONES

In 1981 when the large mainframe computer corporation, IBM, introduced the model 5150 personal computer, or "PC" as it was called, the market was well-developed, but in need of standardization. It took a major company such as IBM to do this. The main contribution of the PC was not a significant advance of technology, but rather standardization of technology. Its five bus expansion ports, Intel 8088 processor with 16 address lines, and 5.25-inch floppy disk drives, while not truly breaking new ground, did become a needed standard for the young industry. Similarly, its new operating system, MicroSoft's Disk Operating System, known as MS-DOS, PC-DOS, or sometimes just DOS, quickly replaced the previous standard. CP/M.

The standardization to MS-DOS, and its adaptation by numerous IBM compatible, or "clone", manufacturers helped expand the personal computer market. IBM's reputation as a manufacturer of serious business computers was a factor in the expansion of personal computers into the business market.

IBM (International Business Machines) 5150 PC (PC1 and PC2)
Processor: Intel 8088, running at 4.77 MHz.
RAM: PC1: 16 K, expandable to 64 K (for a few hundred dollars). PC2: 64 K, expandable to 256 K.
Display: 11.5-inch, monitor, in color or black-and-white, displaying upper and lower case characters in 25 rows of 80 characters each.
Operator input: 83-key keyboard with numeric keypad and 10 function keys.
Data storage: Cassette or one or two 5.24-inch floppy drives of 160 K each. Later one or two 360 K floppy drives were standard.
Physical: 20"W by 16"D by 5.5"H, weighed 21 pounds without drives, and 28 pounds with 2 drives.
Production: Introduced on August 12 of 1981, and was available by October. The PC1 version was discontinued about March of 1983. Between August and September of 1981 about 13,000 5150s were sold. It was discontinued on April 2, 1987.
Cost: Prices ranged from $1355 for the very basic 64 K system, up to about $6000.

(cont.)

IBM 5150 PC CPU

5150 internal view

Complete IBM 5150 PC

5150 front-panel label

5150 original packaging had separate
boxes for keyboard, CPU and monitor

*The 5150 was one of the most important computers ever produced, and
was perhaps the most important personal computer. It brought standardization to the microcomputer industry, both in hardware and software and
ushered in a new period of growth. It had BASIC in ROM. Much software
was offered by IBM at introduction, including VisiCalc and Easy Writer.
It was first sold in ComputerLand stores, then in Sears and Macy's. It had
five bus expansion ports.*

Value: $200 to $300 for 16 K to 64 K machine, **$125 to $175** for 64 K to
↑56 K machine. Must have IBM monitor and keyboard.

Wang Laboratories Professional Computer (PC)
Processor: Intel 8086.
RAM: 128 K, expandable to 640 K.
Display: 12-inch black-and-white or color TV, displaying 25 lines of 80 characters each.
Data storage: 5.25-inch double-sided, double-density floppy drive with 360 K capacity. Five M or 10 M Winchester drives were available.
Physical: 23.1" by 14.9" by 6.5", weighed 27.8 pounds.
Production: Introduced in May of 1982. Discontinued in 1988.
Cost: $2595 for the single floppy system without a monitor, $3265 for the single floppy system with a monitor, $3790 for the dual floppy system with a monitor, and $5650 for a single floppy system with a 10 M Winchester drive.

This machine had five expansion slots, a parallel port and an RS-232 serial port.

Value: $75-$150

Columbia Data Products MPC 1600-4
Processor: Intel 8088.
RAM: Up to 256 K.
Data storage: 10 M hard drive.
Production: In production by 1984.
Cost: $4770.

The 1600-4 had 8 expansion slots, 2 serial ports and a parallel port. It was important in that it was the first IBM PC clone.

Value: $50-$125

TI (Texas Instruments) Professional Computer
Processor: Intel 8088 running at 5 MHz.
RAM: 64 K, expandable to over 700 K.
Display: 12-inch black-and-white or 13-inch color monitor displaying 25 lines of 80 characters each.
Operator input: 97-key keyboard with numeric keypad and 12 programmable function keys.
Data storage: Built-in 320 K 5.25-inch floppy drive. 5 M, 10 M, or 15 M Winchester drive available.
Physical: 19" W by 17" D by 5.75" H.
Production: Introduced in January of 1983.
Cost: $2195 for unit with 64 K, keyboard, black-and-white monitor, and one 320 K floppy.

This machine ran either version 1.1 of MS-DOS or CP/M-86. It had up to 6 expansion slots, a parallel port and a serial port.

Value: $75-$150

5160 CPU with half-height 20 M hard drive

5160 front-panel label.
The XT CPU carried a
different front panel label
than the PC.

5160 internal view

This keyboard was used on
some late XTs.

IBM (International Business Machines) 5160 PC XT
Processor: Intel 8088.
RAM: 128 K, expandable to 640 K.
Display: 12.5-inch color monitor.
Operator input: 83-key keyboard with numeric keypad and 10 function
keys was standard on early units. Later a 101-key keyboard was
available.
Data storage: Double sided 360 K floppy drive and 10 M or 20 M
hard drive. Initially the 5160 could not be bought without a hard
drive, but later it became an option, as was a 3.5-inch 720 K floppy
drive. Early floppy drives were full-height, later they were half-height.
Physical: 20" L by 16" D by 6" H, weighed 32 pounds.
Production: Introduced March 8, 1983.
Cost: Prices ranged from $1395 to $4995.

*This updated version of the original PC had 8 expansion slots, and the
cassette port of the earlier machines was deleted. The initials XT stood for*

Extended Technology. It initially used version 2.0 of DOS. As with the PC, it had BASIC in ROM, and an expansion port for the Intel 8087 math co-processor. A serial interface was available in the enhanced models. The 5162 model, which had 640 K RAM, a 20 M hard drive in addition to it's 80286 processor, is discussed later under the XT 286 heading.

Value: $300-$400 for the standard 20 M hard-drive unit with 640 K. For units with less memory and 10 M or smaller hard-drives may range down to $125. Must have IBM monitor and keyboard.

Eagle PC-E
Processor: Intel 8088, running at 4.77 MHz.
RAM: 64 K.
Display: Black-and-white.
Operator input: Keyboard with 24 function keys.
Data storage: 5.25-inch double-sided 320 K floppy drive.
Production: In production by 1983.
Cost: $1995

This machine had two serial ports, a parallel port, and one bus expansion slot.

Value: $50-$125

Eagle PC-1
Processor: Intel 8088, running at 4.77 MHz.
RAM: 128 K, expandable to 512 K.
Display: Black-and-white.
Operator input: Keyboard with 24 function keys.
Data storage: One 5.25-inch floppy drive.
Cost: $2995.
Production: In production by 1983.

This machine ran MS-DOS and CP/M-86 operating systems. It had two serial ports, one parallel port, and one expansion slot.

Value: $50-$125

Eagle PC-2
Processor: Intel 8088, running at 4.77 MHz.
RAM: 128 K, expandable to 512 K.
Display: Black-and-white.
Operator input: Keyboard with 24 function keys.
Data storage: Two 5.25-inch floppy drives.
Production: In production by 1983.
Cost: $3495

This machine ran MS-DOS and CP/M-86 operating systems. It had two serial ports, one parallel port, and one expansion slot.

Value: $50-$125

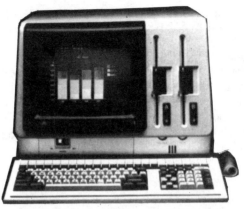

NEC (Nippon Electric Co.) APC (Advanced Personal Computer)
Processor: 16 bit.
Display: Color monitor.
Data storage: 8-inch floppy drive.
Production: In production by 1983.
Cost: $3998.

Value: $75-$150

Eagle PC-XL
Processor: Intel 8088, running at 4.77 MHz.
RAM: 128 K, expandable to 512 K.
Display: Black-and-white monitor.
Operator input: Keyboard with 24 function keys.
Data storage: One 5.25-inch floppy drive, and one 10 M hard drive.
Production: In production by 1983.
Cost: $4495.

The PC-XL had two serial ports, one parallel port, and one expansion slot.
Value: $50-$125

HP (Hewlett-Packard) 150
Processor: Intel 8088, running at 8 MHz.
RAM: 256 K, expandable to 640 K.
Display: CRT displayed 24 rows of 80 characters each. Graphics mode
had a resolution of 512 by 390 pixels.
Operator input: Keyboard and touchscreen.
Data storage: Two 3.5-inch floppy disk drives gave 540 K of storage,
and 5 M and 15 M hard drives were available.
Production: Introduced in 1983.

*The 150 ran MS-DOS 2.11. It had two expansion slots, an IEEE-488 and
dual RS232 interfaces.*
Value: $100-$150

IBM (International Business Machines) 370 XT

Processor: Intel 8088, and two Motorola 68000s.
RAM: 640 K.
Display: Monochrome or color.
Operator input: Keyboard.
Data storage: Floppy disk and 10 M or 20 M hard drives.
Physical: Basically the same as a standard XT.
Production: Introduced on October 18, 1983.
Cost: $9000 with 10 M hard drive, or $3800 to upgrade an XT to 370 specifications.

This was basically a conventional XT chassis with three custom cards to allow the machine to emulate IBM mainframe System 370 instructions. Modes could be switched by using a special key sequence. Two modified Motorola processors were used on the special cards.

Value: Comparable to similarly-equipped XT.

IBM 3270 PC

Processor: Intel 8088.
Display: Had Extended Graphics Adapter (XGA) card to display graphics in resolution up to 720 by 350 or 640 by 200 pixels.
Operator input: A special keyboard with more keys than the standard PC, and an altered layout. It included 20 function keys at the top of the keyboard. Color coding of labels denoted PC and 3270 functions. The keyboard was connected to a separate expansion card, rather than to the motherboard as on a standard PC.
Physical: Basically the same as a standard XT.
Production: Announced on October 18 of 1983.
Cost: $5900

The 3270 was a version of the XT designed to exchange information with the IBM 370, to which it was designed to be connected. It was essentially a conventional XT with from three to six custom cards. It ran the "3270 PC Control Program," which could simultaneously run four remote mainframe sessions, one PC DOS program, and two electronic notepads. Information could be moved between windows.

Value: Comparable to similarly-equipped XT.

NEC (Nippon Electric Co.) PC-100
Processor: Intel 8086, running at 8 MHz.
RAM: 128 K, expandable to 768 K.
Display: Color displaying 32 lines of 90 characters per line in its horizontal installation, or 45 lines of 64 characters per line in the vertical installation.
Operator input: 91-key keyboard with numeric keypad and 5 function keys.
Data storage: One or two 360 K 5.25-inch floppy drives.
Production: Introduced in October of 1983.

This machine had 4 expansion slots and parallel and serial (RS232C) interfaces.

Value: $75-$150

Tandy/Radio Shack TRS-80 Model 2000
Processor: Intel 80186, running at 8 MHz.
RAM: 128 K, expandable to 768 K for the basic system, 256 K, expandable to 768 K for the HD system.
Display: CRT displaying 8 colors at a resolution of 640 by 400 pixels
Data storage: Two 5.25-inch floppy drives for the standard system, or one floppy and a 10 M hard drive for the HD system.
Production: Introduced in November of 1983.
Cost: $2750 for the standard system, $4250 for the HD system.

The Model 2000 ran version 2.0 of the MS-DOS operating system. It had an RS-232 port.

Value: $50-$125

IBM 4860 PCjr
Processor: Intel 8088, running at 4.77 MHz.
RAM: 64 K, expandable to 128 K.
Display: Color TV displaying 25 lines of 40 or 80 characters per line. The model 4863 color monitor was also available.
Operator input: A 62-key "Chicklet" keyboard connected to the computer by infrared transmission (using 4 AA batteries) or through an optional cable. A more conventional keyboard was also available.
Data storage: 360 K double-sided 5.25-inch floppy drive.
Physical: Weighed 13 pounds, 6 ounces.
Production: Introduced in November of 1983.
Cost: $669, or $1269 for the enhanced version.

This was IBM's second basic PC design. Despite several reworks, it was not a sales success. It ran most, but not all, IBM PC software. It had two ports for ROM cartridges containing software.

Value: $25-$100

(cont.)

4860 front-panel label

Complete IBM 4860 PCjr

IBM 4860 PCjr CPU

(cont.)

4860 internal view

Later-style 4860 keyboard

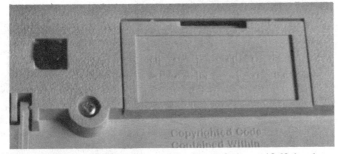

Port for batteries to power the IR signal from a 4860 keyboard and the CPU

(cont.)

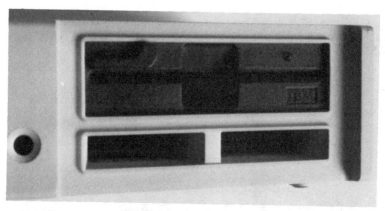

4860 data storage, floppy-drive over two ROM-cartridge ports

IBM ROM cartridge for the 4860

4863 color-monitor front-panel label

Data General Model 10
Processor: microECLIPSE and Intel 8086.
RAM: 128 K, or 256 K.
Display: Color monitor displaying 24 lines of 80 characters each.
Operator input: Keyboard.
Data storage: One or two 360 K 5.25-inch floppy drives. 15 M Winchester drive.
Physical: Comprised of interlocking modules, each with dimensions 4.8" by 12.8" by 10.7".
Production: Introduced late 1983.

This machine had 5 expansion slots.

Value: $50-$125

Zenith Data Systems Z-151
Processor: Intel 8088, running at 4.77 MHz.
Production: Introduced about late 1983.

The Z-151 was Zenith's first DOS machine.

Value: $50-$150

Wordplex Desktop PC
Production: Introduced in November of 1983.

Value: $50-$125

Electro Design IMP-6
Processor: Intel 8088
Display: Color.
Data storage: Two external double-sided, double-density floppy drives.
Cost: $3144.
Production: In production by 1984.

This machine had 12 expansion slots.

Value: $50-$125

ITT Xtra
Processor: Intel 8088.
RAM: 128 K, expandable to 640 K.
Data storage: One or two floppy drives, and a 10 M hard-drive was available.
Production: In production by 1984.

This machine ran MS-DOS 2.0.

Value: $50-$75

MAD (Modular Advanced Design) 1
Processor: Intel 80186, running at 7.2 MHz.
RAM: 128 K.
Display: Black-and-white monitor, but could support color.
Operator input: Keyboard with 10 function keys.
Data storage: Two double-density, double-sided 360 K floppy drives, and a 10 M hard drive.
Production: In production by 1984.
Cost: $4295 with two floppies, $6195 with hard drive.

The MAD-1 ran version 2.0 of the MS-DOS operating system. It had one expansion slot, two RS-232 serial ports, and one parallel port.
Value: $50-$125

Mindset Corp. Personal Computer
Processor: Intel 80186, running at 6 MHz.
RAM: 32 K, expandable to 256 K.
Display: Color TV.
Operator input: 84-key keyboard with 10 function keys.
Data storage: Two cartridge slots and one 360 K 5.25-inch floppy drive.
Physical: 16" by 12.2" by 2.8", weighed 6 pounds. With the expansion unit the dimensions were 16" by 12.2" by 2.5"; and the weight was 7.5 pounds with one floppy drive, or 11 pounds with two floppies.
Production: Introduced in 1984.
Cost: About $1200 for the cartridge only system, about $2000 for the one-disk system, about $2600 two-disk system with 256 K.

The MS-DOS 2.0 operating system was optional for this machine. It had three I/O module slots, and took cartridges that could contain ROM, RAM with battery backup, or a combination of both. An expansion unit was available to add 96 K, one or two floppy drives, and three I/O module slots.
Value: $50-$100

AT&T PC 6300
Processor: Intel 8088.
Production: Introduced on June 26, 1984.

The 6300 was AT&T's first DOS machine.

Value: $75-$175

Mitsubishi
Processor: Intel 8088, running at 4.77 MHz or 7.16 MHz.
Production: In production by 1984.

This machine was sold by Sperry and Leading Edge.

Value: $50-$125

Leading Edge Products Personal Computer
Processor: Intel 8088, running at 4.77 MHz or 7.16 MHz.
RAM: 128 K.
Display: 12-inch black-and-white monitor.
Operator input: Keyboard.
Data storage: Two double-sided double-density 320 K floppy drives.
Cost: $2895.
Production: In production by 1984.

This machine ran version of 1.25 of the MS-DOS operating system, had one parallel port, one serial port, and seven expansion slots.

Eagle 1600   **Value: $50-$125**
Processor: Intel 8086, running at 8 MHz.
RAM: 128 K.
Display: Monochrome monitor displaying 720-by-352 pixel resolution.
Operator input: Keyboard with 24 function keys.
Data storage: 800 K 5.25-inch floppy drive and hard drive with 12.5 M capacity.
Production: In production by 1984.
Cost: $6995 with 10 M hard drive, $8995 with 32 M hard drive.
The 1600 had 8 expansion slots.

Value: $50-$150

Digigraphic Systems Corp Extra-70
Processor: Intel 8088.
RAM: 256 K.
Display: Black-and-white monitor.
Data storage: Two double-sided double-density 5.25-inch floppy drives and a 10 M hard drive. A 60 M hard drive was optional.
Production: In production by 1984.
Cost: $10,694 with the 60 M drive, $6695 without the 60 M drive.

The Extra-70 had 10 expansion slots, 3 occupied with system boards. It had 2 serial ports and a parallel port.

Value: $50-$175

Sanyo MBC-555
Processor: Intel 8088, running at 3.6 MHz.
RAM: 128 K, expandable to 256 K.
Display: Black-and-white or color.
Operator input: Keyboard with numeric keypad and 5 function keys.
Data storage: Single-sided double-density floppy drive.
Cost: Under $1000 for the single-drive system.
Production: In production by 1984.

This machine ran version of 1.25 of the MS-DOS operating system and had one parallel port.

Value: $75-$150

Sperry Personal Computer
Processor: Intel 8088, running at 4.77 or 7.16 MHz.
Display: Color monitor. Could display CGA (320-by-200 pixels), or Sperry high-resolution (640-by-400 pixels), with 256 colors.
Operator input: Keyboard with LED status lights.
Cost: $2643 to $5753.
Production: Introduced in 1983.

This machine ran version 1.25 of the MS-DOS operating system.
Value: $75-$150

Tava Corp PC
RAM: 256 K.
Data storage: Two double-sided floppy drives.
Production: In production by 1984.
Cost: $2395.

This machine had five expansion slots, two serial ports, and one parallel port.
Value: $50-$125

Electro Design IMP-12
Processor: Intel 8088.
Display: Color monitor.
Data storage: One double-sided, double-density floppy drive and one 10 M Winchester drive.
Production: In production by 1984.
Cost: $5456.

The IMP-12 had 12 expansion slots.
Value: $50-$125

Pronto Series 16
Processor: Intel 80186, running at 8 MHz.
Data storage: Two floppy drives had a capacity of 800 K each.
Production: In production by 1984.
Cost: $3750.

The Series 16 ran MS-DOS 2.0.
Value: $50-$125

Toshiba T-33300
Processor: Intel 8088.
RAM: 192 K, expandable to 512 K.
Display: Monochrome monitor standard, color monitor optional for $700. The resolution of both monitors was 650 by 500 pixels.
Data storage: One to two floppy drives.
Production: In production by 1984.
Cost: The single-drive was $2495, and the two-drive version was $3190.

This machine ran MS-DOS 2.0.
Value: $50-$125

Wyse WY-1000
Processor: Intel 80186, running at 8 MHz.
RAM: 128 K, expandable to 768 K.
Display: Wyse terminal.
Data storage: Floppy drives with IBM format, a 10 M hard-drive was optional.
Production: In production by 1984.
Cost: Base price without terminal and with one floppy drive was $1995. With two floppies and the WY-50 terminal it was $3995.
This machine ran DOS 2.1.

Value: $50-$125

Zenith Data Systems Z-159
Display: Supported EGA video display.
Operator input: 101-key keyboard.
Production: Introduced about 1986.

The Z-159 was similar to the Z-158. It could be adapted to 80286 processor.
Value: $50-$125

Zenith Data Systems eaZy PC
Processor: NEC V20 CPU.
RAM: 512K, expandable to 640 with 128 K Memory Expansion Module.
Display: Monochrome CRT with 16 grayscales, with a resolution of 640-by-200 pixels. The video circuitry was on the motherboard.
Production: Had been out of production for some time by late 1989.

The eaZy PC came in three models, the PC-1, PC-2 and PC-3. Serial port and mode modules were also available.
Value: $30-$75

Stearns Computer Systems PC
Processor: Intel 8086.
Display: A 15-inch black-and-white CRT displaying 25 lines of 80 characters each, or 55 lines of 80 characters each.
Operator input: Keyboard with function keys and LED status lights.
Data storage: Both floppy and hard drives.
Production: In production by 1984.
Cost: $4995 with 10 M hard drive, $5995 with 20 M hard drive.

The Stearns PC ran version 1.25 of the ST-DOS operating system, and would also run PC-DOS. It had a 16-bit data bus.
Value: $50-$125

Panasonic JB 3000
Production: In production by 1984.
The JB-3000 was marketed in Australia.

Value: $50-$100

Zenith Data Systems Z-148
Production: Introduced about 1985.

This machine was basically a Z-157 in a different box. Its expansion slots were available only through a separate daughter board, which was typically used to add an HDD and controller.

Value: $30-$75

Zenith Data Systems Z-157
Production: Introduced about 1985

The Z-157 was expandable with a daughterboard.

Value: $30-$75

Zenith Data Systems Z-158
Production: Introduced about 1985.

The Z-158 had the same appearance as the Z-151, but was switchable between 4.77 and 8 MHz. This was perhaps the first "turbo" system by a major manufacturer.

Value: $50-$125

AT&T 6300 Plus
Production: Introduced in October of 1985.

Value: $50-$125

The 5162 had the same case as the 8088-based machines

The keyboard from a Model 286

IBM 5162 PC XT (Model 286)
Processor: Intel 80286, running at 6 MHz.
RAM: 640 K, expandable up to 15.5 M.
Operator input: IBM's Enhanced Keyboard with indicator lights.
Data storage: Half-height 1.2 M 5.25-inch double-sided floppy drive
and a 20 M hard drive. A third drive was available from among 720 K
or 1.44 M 3.5-inch drives or 360 K or 1.2 M 5.25-inch drives.
Physical: Had the appearance of an XT. 19.6" L by 16.1" D by 5.5"
H, and weighed 28 pounds.
Production: Introduced September 9, 1986.
Cost: $2495 with 1.2 M floppy and 20 M hard drive.

This machine was basically a lower-priced AT. It had 16-bit expansion slots,
serial and parallel ports, BASIC in ROM, and a battery-powered real-time
clock. **Value: Comparable to similarly-equipped XT.**

170

II-4. IBM AT AND CLONES

In 1982 Intel introduced the successor to the 8088, the 80286. This new processor had 16-bit external data lines, and an improved instruction set. In 1984 IBM introduced the new AT (Advanced Technology) personal computer based on the 80286. It had an expanded 16-bit bus architecture, ran at 6 MHz, up from the 4.77 MHz of the PC and PC XT that preceded it, and came with a new high-density 1.22 M byte 5.25-inch floppy drive and a 40 M byte hard disk drive. As with the PC and XT, numerous clone manufacturers followed IBM's lead.

IBM 5170 PC AT
Processor: Intel 80286, running first at 6 MHz and later at 8 MHz.
RAM: 256 K in the standard machine and 512 K in the enhanced machine. Expandable to 16 M.
Display: CRT.
Operator input: 84-key or 101-key keyboard.
Data storage: 5.25-inch 1.2 M floppy drive. 20 M and 30 M harddrives available in the enhanced machine.
Physical: 21.25" L by 17.28" D by 6.38" H. The base unit weighed 37 pounds, and the enhanced unit weighed 42 pounds (with a 20 M or 30 M hard drive).
Cost: The 6 MHz machine with 256 K and a 1.2 M floppy drive was $3395. With a 20 M hard drive it was $4895, and with a 30 M hard drive it was $5295. Later, the 8 MHz machine with 512 K and a 30 M hard drive was available for $3595.
Production: Introduced on August 14, 1984. The 30 M machine, with a new style of motherboard, came out on October 2, 1985. On April 2, 1986 the 8 MHz machines were introduced. These had the 101-key keyboard.

AT stands for Advanced Technology. It had the ability to use 16 MB of

(cont.)

IBM 5170 (cont.)

external memory, not addressable by DOS. It had eight expansion slots: six 16-bit slots and two 8-bit slots. This successor to the XT was considerably advanced over the old design.

Value: $400-$600 for the standard 20 or 30 M hard-drive units with 640 K. For units with less memory and no hard-drive prices may range down to $200. Must have IBM monitor and keyboard.

IBM 3270 AT

IBM 3270 AT keyboard

Plastic back-panel cover on a 3270 AT

IBM 3270 front-panel label

IBM 3270 AT
Processor: Intel 80286.
Physical: Sometimes had plastic covers on the back.
Production: Announced June 18, 1985.

This machine was basically the same as the 3270 XT, except that it was based on the AT.

Value: Comparable to similarly-equipped AT.

Zenith Data Systems Z-241
Processor: Intel 80286, running at 6 MHz.
Display: External monitor.
Production: Introduced about 1985.

The Z-241 was possibly Zenith's first AT-compatable machine.

Value: $100-$200

IBM 370 AT
Production: Introduced about 1985.

This machine was basically the same as the 370 XT, except that it was based on the AT.

Value: Comparable to similarly-equipped AT

ALR (Advanced Logic Research) Access 386
Processor: Intel 80386
Production: Introduced in 1986.

This was likely the first 80386-based machine.

Value: $500-$1500, depending on configuration

Zenith Data Systems Z-248
Processor: Intel 80286, running at 8 MHz.
Operator input: External monitor.
Production: Introduced about 1986.

Value: $50-$125

Zenith Data Systems Z-286
Processor: Intel 80286.
Display: External Monitor.
Production: Introduced about 1986.

Value: $100-$200

Compaq Deskpro 386
Processor: Intel 80386.
Production: Introduced September of 1986.

This was Compaq's first 80386-based machine.

Value $500-$1500, depending on configuration.

AT&T 6310
Processor: Intel 80286.
Production: Introduced February 17, 1987.

Value: $50-$125

AT&T 6312 WGS
Production: Was in production by 1987.
WGS stood for Work Group Station.

Value $100-$200

Zenith Data Systems Z-386/16
Processor: Intel 80386, running at 16 MHz.
Display: External monitor.
Production: Introduced in late 1987 or early 1988.
Value: $500-$1500 depending on configuration.

II-5. MACHINES WITH GRAPHIC USER-INTERFACE

Despite IBM's influence on the personal computer market, other types of systems continued to be developed. The introduction of the Apple Lisa in 1982, and the Macintosh in 1984, with their graphical user interfaces, or GUI, made operation of a personal computer much simpler than before. The GUI machines operated pictorially on the screen by moving a cursor with a mouse. Requiring little knowledge of computers to operate, these machines further expanded the market for personal computers, bringing them yet closer to being a consumer item.

Xerox Alto
Operator input: Keyboard and mouse.
Production: This machine came out in 1974, and some claim it was the first PC. It was never sold commercially, however, and less than 2000 were produced.

The Alto had a mouse and Ethernet.

Value: $1000-$1500

Apple Lisa 1
Processor: Motorola MC68000, running at 5 MHz.
RAM: 1 M, expandable to 2 M.
Display: Integral black-and-white 12-inch bit-mapped display.
Data storage: Two 860 K 5.25-inch floppy drives. A 5 M hard drive, called Profile, was available.
Production: Introduced in January of 1983. In January of 1985 it was renamed Macintosh XL. It was discontinued in April of 1985.
Cost: $9995

Lisa stood for Local Integrated Software Architecture. This was Apple's first GUI machine, and a precurser to the very popular Macintosh. Thus it was an important machine. It had three expansion slots, one parallel port and two programmable serial ports. It had up to 12 menus available on a menu bar.

Value: $50-$150

Apple Lisa 2
Processor: Motorola 68000.
RAM: 512 K.
Display: Black-and-white bit-mapped screen.
Operator input: Keyboard with numeric keypad.
Data storage: 3.5-inch 400 K floppy drive, 5 and 10 M hard drives available.
Production: In production by 1984.
Cost: $3495, $4495 with the 5 M drive (Lisa 2/5), and $5495 with the 10 M drive (Lisa 2/10).

A Macintosh operating system was optional for this updated Lisa.

Value: $75-$175

Macintosh

Macintosh keyboard

Apple Macintosh 128
Processor: Motorola 68000, running at 7.83 MHz.
RAM: 128 K.
Display: 9-inch black-and-white bitmapped display. Resolution was 512 by 342 pixels.
Operator input: 58-key keyboard (59 in the international version), and a mouse.
Data storage: 3.5-inch 400 K single-sided floppy drive.
Production: This machine was announced in early 1983, and released for sale January 1984. It was upgraded to an Enhanced version in April of 1986.
Cost: $2495. The Enhanced version sold for $1999.

This was the first popular GUI machine, and it gave rise to the very successful line of Apple Macintosh machines. It had two serial ports.
Value: $200-$300

Apple Macintosh 512
Processor: Motorola 68000.
RAM: 512 K.
Display: 9-inch black-and-white bitmapped display.
Data storage: 3.5-inch 400 K floppy drive.
Physical: 13.4" H by 10" W by 11" D.
Production: Introduced in September of 1984.

This enhanced version of the original 128 K Macintosh was nicknamed the "Fat Mac."

Value: $300-$400

Commodore   Amiga 1000
Production: Introduced in 1985.
Cost: $1295

Value: $100-$200

Apple Macintosh Plus
Data storage: 800 K floppy drive.
Cost: $2599.
Production: Introduced in January of 1986.

Value: $400-$600

II-6. PORTABLES

An important side development of the personal computer was the portable, which allowed the now-addicted personal-computer user to take their machine with them. One of the first machines designed specifically with portability in mind was the Baby!, a computer packaged in a small suitcase. This early machine required a separate CRT, and was shown being carried along with a small television to demonstrate its portability. It was followed by various similarly-sized machines with increasing functionally (built-in CRTs and disk drives, for example). These machines are now classed as "luggables," or sometimes just as "portables." This latter word also applies to mobile machines in general, as opposed to "desktops" which are stationary machines.

II-6.1. LUGGABLES

The luggables were portable machines roughly the size of a small suitcase. Their weights typically ranged between 20 to 30 pounds, and they usually were operated on a desktop using AC power.

STM Systems BABY! 1
Processor: 6502.
RAM: 2 K, expandable to 60 K. Additional 4 K static ram was available for $205.
Display: 9-inch video display interface with 16 lines of 32 7-by-9 pixel characters.
Operator input: 63-key keyboard.
Data storage: A 1200-Baud tape interface was standard and a 90 K 5.25-inch floppy drive with power supply and controller was available for $750.
Physical: The dimensions of the Lucite case within the briefcase were: 14.5" W by 10" D by 4.5" H. The weight of the computer without the briefcase was 10 pounds.
Production: Was introduced about August of 1976.
Cost: $850 completely assembled with 2 K, or $1000 with 4 K.

While many early machines could easily be carried, this machine was likely the first personal computer to be sold specifically as a portable. It was shipped in a Lucite box inside a briefcase, but required a cassette recorder and a television monitor to operate. Its single-board motherboard was located underneath the keyboard, which sat along the bottom of the case. It had a 512 K bootstrap loader in ROM. Up to 4 K of ROM could be mounted on the motherboard. It had four parallel ports, and RS-232 and 20 mA serial ports.

Value: $300-$500

Digital Electronics Corp DE68
Processor: Motorola 6800.
RAM: 1 K byte, could be expanded to 32 K.
Display: 20-column-wide alphanumeric display.
Operator input: 96-character keyboard.
Data storage: Miniature digital cassette with 100 K byte storage.
Cost: $3500.
Production: Was introduced about November of 1976.

This stand-alone computer was housed in a briefcase. It had a 5.5 K byte PROM operating system.

Value: $150-$300

RDA PRD11
Processor: LSI-11.
RAM: 32 K, expandable to 56 K.
Display: Could support multiple terminal interfaces.
Operator input: Through terminal interfaces.
Data storage: Tape.
Physical: This 23-pound machine was housed in an aluminum suitcase.
Production: Introduced about November of 1977.
Cost: $4950.

Available software for this machine included FORTRAN IV and multiuser BASIC. It had a serial interface.

Value: $150-$250

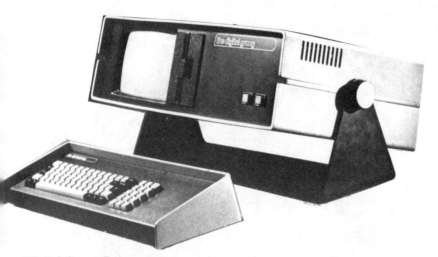

Digital Group Bytemaster
Processor: Zilog Z-80, running at 2.5 MHz.
RAM: 18 K, expandable to 34 K.
Display: Built-in 9-inch CRT, displaying 16 lines of 64 characters each.
Operator input: Keyboard with numeric keypad.
Data storage: Cassette of 5.25-inch floppy drive. Later a hard drive was available.
Physical: Housed in a metal cabinet.
Production: Announced in 1978.
Cost: $1995 as a kit including a cassette drive, $2895 assembled including a 5.25-inch floppy drive.

The Bytemaster had a proprietary bus and four parallel ports.
Value: $150-$300

Quasar Data Products Micro-Information System
Processor: 6502, running at 1 MHz.
RAM: 2 K, expandable to 4 K.
Display: LCD, displaying 1 line of 26 characters. Video display in case.
Operator input: 65-key keyboard, with three programmable function keys.
Data storage: Cassette.
Physical: System was contained in a briefcase.
Production: Was in production in late 1980.

This machine was comprised of the Quasar hand-held computer, along with a display, modem and cassette all contained in a briefcase.
Value: $100-$150

Osborne 1 with bottom of case open, showing keyboard, monitor and disk drives.

Top: Osborne 1 with case closed-up, showing carrying handle. The black compartment next to the handle contains the power cord. Right: Osborne 1 with optional external monitor. It attaches at the lower left of the integral monitor.

(cont.)

Osborne 1
Processor: Zilog Z-80A.
RAM: 64 K.
Display: Black-and-white integral 5-inch CRT displayed 24 lines of 52 characters each. A larger monitor was available as an option.
Operator input: Keyboard with numeric keypad and 10 programmable function keys.
Data storage: Two integral 5.25-inch floppy drives, each storing 91 K.
Physical: This unit was the size of a large briefcase, and weighed 23.5 pounds. It could run on AC or DC voltages, and a battery pack was optional.
Production: Introduced in April of 1981 at the West Coast Computer Faire. Sales went from $0 to $100 million in less than two years. On September 13, 1983, the company went bankrupt.
Cost: $1795.

The Osborne 1 was the first popular portable. It ran the CP/M operating system, and came with BASIC, MicroPro's Word Star and SuperCalc. It had both IEEE-488 and RS232C interfaces.

Value: $50-$125

Compaq with the bottom open showing the keyboard, monitor and disk drives. One of the two sliding-doors is open to show expansion cards.

The Compaq shown closed up.

The Compaq with its carrying case. The leather covering on the handle is not original.

Compaq Portable

Processor: Intel 8088, running at 4.77 MHz.

RAM: 128 K, expandable to 256 K.

Display: 9-inch black-and-white monitor displaying 25 lines of 80 characters each.

Operator input: 83-key keyboard, with numeric keypad and 10 programmable function keys.

Data storage: One or two integral double-sided 5.25-inch floppy drives with 320 K capacity each. One drive was the standard configuration.

Physical: 20" by 8.5" by 15.3", weighed 28 pounds.

Production: Introduced in November of 1982. Production began in January of 1983 and ended in November of 1987.

Cost: $2995 for the basic system, $3590 for the two-drive system.

This was the first portable IBM-compatible computer. It ran version 1.1 of the MS-DOS operating system, had five expansion slots and a parallel interface. **Value: $75-$150**

184

Comterm Hyperion
Processor: Intel 8088.
RAM: 256 K.
Display: Integral 7-inch black-and-white monitor displaying 25 lines of 80 characters per line.
Operator input: Keyboard with function keys.
Data storage: Two integral 5.25-inch floppy drives.
Physical: This unit weighed about 20 pounds.
Production: In production by 1983.
Cost: $3195 with one drive, $3690 with two drives.

This portable PC-compatible ran version 1.1 of the MS-DOS operating system. It had a serial port and a parallel port. There were no expansion slots, but a connector allowed connection to an expansion box with 7 slots and a Winchester hard disk.

Value: $75-$125

Otrona Attache
Display: Integral 5-inch black-and-white monitor displaying 24 lines of 80 characters each.
Operator input: Keyboard.
Data storage: Two built-in 380 K floppy drives.
Physical: Weighed 18 pounds.
Production: In production by 1983.
Cost: $3995.

This portable ran the CP/M operating system.

Value: $25-$75

Non-Linear Systems/Kaypro Corp II
Processor: Zilog Z-80.
RAM: 64 K.
Display: Integral 9-inch black-and-white monitor displaying 24 lines of 80 characters each.
Operator input: Keyboard with numeric keypad.
Data storage: Two built-in 5.25-inch single-density 191 K floppy drives.
Physical: This unit was about the size of a briefcase, and weighed 26 pounds.
Production: Was in production by 1983.
Cost: $1795.

This early portable was very similar to the Osborne 1, which it followed. It ran the CP/M operating system, and had both RS232 and parallel ports.
Value: $25-$75

Seequa Chameleon
Processor: Intel 8088 and Zilog Z-80.
RAM: 128 K, expandable to 256 K.
Display: 9-inch phosphor monitor.
Data storage: Two single-sided 5.25-inch floppy drives.
Physical: 8" by 8" by 16", and weighed 26 pounds.
Production: Introduced in 1983.
Cost: $1995.

This machine ran both the DOS and CP/M operating systems. It had one parallel port and one serial port.

Value: $50-$125

Tandy/Radio Shack TRS-80 Model 4P
RAM: 64 K.
Display: Displayed 24 lines of 80 characters each.
Data storage: Two floppy disks with 184 K capacity each.
Production: Introduced in September of 1983.
Cost: $1795.

Value: $25-$75

Compaq   Compaq Plus
Processor: Intel 8088.
RAM: 128 K, expandable to 256 K.
Display: 9-inch black-and-white monitor.
Data storage: 320 K floppy drive, and 10 M hard drive.
Production: Introduced in October of 1983.
Cost: $4995.

This machine had three expansion slots, and a parallel interface. It ran the MS-DOS operating system.

Value: $75-$150

Wordplex Portable PC
RAM: 128 K, expandable to 512 K.
Display: Nine-inch monitor.
Data storage: Double-sided floppy disk gave 320 K of storage. A second floppy and a 10 M hard drive were available.
Physical: Weighed 28 pounds.
Production: Introduced in November of 1983.

Value: $25-$75

Eagle Spirit XL
Processor: Intel 8088.
RAM: 128 K, expandable to 640 K.
Display: Black-and-white 9-inch.
Operator input: Keyboard with LED status lights.
Data storage: 320 K floppy drive and 10 M hard drive.
Physical: Weighed 32.5 pounds.
Production: Introduced in October of 1983.
Cost: $4795.

This machine had four expansion slots, two serial interfaces and a parallel interface. It ran both the MS-DOS and CP/M-86 operating systems.
Value: $50-$125

Corona Data Systems Portable PC
Processor: Intel 8088.
RAM: 128 K, expandable to 256 K.
Display: 9-inch black-and-white display.
Operator input: Keyboard.
Data storage: Two 320 K 5.25-inch floppy drives.
Production: In production by 1984.
Cost: $2495.

This portable ran the MS-DOS operating system. It had four expansion slots, and both parallel and serial interfaces.
Value: $30-$75

**Columbia Data Products Columbia Portable VP (Very Personal)
Computer**
Processor: Intel 8088.
RAM: 128 K, expandable to 256 K.
Display: 9-inch black-and-white monitor.
Operator input: Keyboard.
Data storage: Two 320 K floppy drives.
Physical: This machine weighed about 35 pounds.
Production: In production by 1984.
Cost: $2995.

This portable ran both the MS-DOS and CP/M-86 operating systems. It had one expansion slot, and both parallel and serial interfaces.
Value: $50-$150

IBM Portable PC Courtesy of International Business Machines
Processor: Intel 8088.
RAM: 256 K.
Display: 9-inch amber composite monitor. Also had a CGA adapter.
Operator input: 83-key keyboard.
Data storage: Two 5.25-inch floppy drives.
Physical: 20" by 17" by 8", weighed 30 pounds. It operated on AC power only (it had no battery).
Production: Was in production by 1984, and was withdrawn on April 2, 1986. Not many of these machines were made.

This portable had eight expansion slots and used an XT motherboard.
Value: $200-$350

Panasonic Senior Partner (RL-H7000)
RAM: 256 K.
Display: 9-inch black-and-white or color monitor.
Data storage: Two double-sided, double-density floppy drives.
Physical: Similar in size to the Compaq.
Production: Was in production by 1984.
Cost: $2495 for the single-drive machine.

This machine had a built-in thermal printer, one serial and one parallel port, and a single optional expansion slot. It ran version 2.0 of the MS-DOS operating system.
Value: $50-$125

Non-Linear Systems/Kaypro Corp 10
Processor: Zilog Z-80, running at 4 MHz.
RAM: 64 K.
Display: 9-inch black-and-white monitor displaying 25 lines of 80 characters each.
Operator input: 75-key keyboard with a 14-key numeric keypad. The keys of the keypad doubled as programmable function keys.
Data storage: Double-sided 390 K floppy drive, and 10 M hard drive.
Physical: 19" by 17" by 9", weighed 30 pounds.
Production: In production by 1984.
Cost: $2795.

This machine ran version 2.2 of the CP/M operating system, with enhancements. It had two RS-232C serial ports, one parallel port, and one light-pen port.

Value: $25-$75

Access
Data storage: Two floppy drives.
Production: In production by 1984.

A modem and printer could be carried on top of the Access. Unlike the Osborne-like machines, the handle was not on the back, but along the top side.

Value: $20-$50

Axtrix
Display: Seven-inch CRT.
Data storage: Two floppy drives with 180 K capacity each. A DS model was available with double-sided disks with 360 K capacity.
Physical: Weighed 33 pounds, including the printer.
Production: In production by 1984.
Cost: $2160.

This machine was earlier sold as the Access Matrix. It came with an acoustic modem and a printer.

Value: $20-$50

Jonos C2100
Processor: Zilog Z-80B, running at 6 MHz.
Data storage: Two 3.5-inch floppy drives, or two 5.25-inch drives with 640 K capacity each.
Production: In production by 1984.
Cost: $3195 with 3.5-inch drives, $3495 with 5.25-inch drives.

A 2150 model was available for $500 more. It could take a 10 M hard drive.
Value: $20-$50

Modular Micros Zorba 7
Display: Seven-inch CRT.
Data storage: Two floppy drives with 410 K capacity each.
Physical: Weighed 22 pounds.
Production: In production by 1984.
Cost: $1595.

Value: $20-$50

Modular Micros Zorba 2000
Display: Nine-inch CRT.
Data storage: Two floppies with 820 K capacity each. A 10 M hard drive was available.
Physical: Weighed 25 pounds.
Production: In production by 1984.
Cost: About $2000

Value: $20-$50

TeleVideo TPC1
Display: Monochrome monitor with 640-by-240 pixel resolution.
Data storage: Two floppy drives with 368 K capacity each.
Production: In production by 1984.
Cost: $1995.

Value: $20-$50

Morrow Designs MD3
Physical: Weighed 24 pounds.
Production: In production by 1984.

The MD3 was basically the Morrow Decision in a portable form.
Value: $20-$50

STM Pied Piper
Processor: Zilog Z-80.
Physical: The disk-drive, keyboard and processor were contained in one module weighing 12.5 pounds, while a monitor, printer and an additional disk were contained in a second unit.
Production: In production by 1984.

Value: $20-$50

Seequa Chameleon Plus
Processor: Intel 8088, running at 5 MHz, and Zilog Z-80A, running at 2.5 MHz.
RAM: 128 K, expandable to 256 K.
Display: 9-inch black-and-white monitor displaying 25 lines of 80 characters each.
Operator input: Keyboard with LED status lights.
Data storage: Two 320 K 5.25-inch floppy drives.
Physical: 8" by 18" by 15.5", weighed 28 pounds.
Production: Was in production by 1984.
Cost: $2895.

This machine ran the CP/M-86 operating system, version 1.25 of the MS-DOS operating system, and version 2.2 of the CP/M-80 operating system. It had both parallel and serial interfaces, and an expansion unit with eight slots was optionally available.

Value: $50-$125

Zenith Data Systems Z-171
Data storage: Two 5.25-inch floppy drives.
Physical: With a weight of around 15 pounds and a size comparable to a lunchbox, the Z-171 was one of the smaller luggables. It was battery powered, and sat vertically when in use, with the keyboard laid in front of it.
Production: Introduced about 1985.

The Z-171 was Zenith's first portable.

Zenith Data Systems Z-138
Processor: Intel 8088, running at 4.77 or 8.0 MHz.
Display: Seven-inch amber monitor.
Production: Introduced about 1985.

This portable was PC compatible.

Value: $50-$125

II-6.2. LAPTOPS

The luggables, essentially repackaged desk-top machines, were not portables as we now think of them. Their heavy weights, AC-power requirements, and the large area they required for operation, limited where they could be transported and used. As mineaturation continued, and battery power became practical, the laptops evolved. Weighing in the 10 to 20 pound range, and with dimensions typically comparable to those of a small briefcase, these were truly portable machines. As their name implies, they could easily be operated while sitting on the lap of the user.

MCM Computers System 700, Model 782 APL
RAM: 8 K.
Display: Integrated plasma alphanumeric display.
Operator input: 46-key keyboard.
Data storage: 200 K bytes on two cassette drives. An external floppy disk drive was available.
Physical: Weighed 20 pounds, and incorporated a battery backup system.
Cost: $4950.
Production: Introduced about December of 1977.

This machine came with a full APL language interpreter and 32 K of ROM. Many software packages were available, including math, statistics, business, a text editor, and games. An RS-232C interface was available for $650.
Value: $100-$175

GRI front view in open notebook

GRI side view in closed notebooks

GRI

Processor: Motorola M6800.
Physical: This machine was battery-powered.
Production: In production by 1978.
Cost: Price of "basic unit" was $299.

This machine was housed in the front of a three-ring notebook. It came with an instruction book and sample programs, "complete with batteries for in-hand operation."

Value: $125-$200

GRiD Systems GRiD
Processor: Intel 8086.
Physical: Weighed 5.4 kg.
Production: Introduced in early 1982.

Value: $75-$150

Teleram T-3000
RAM: 128 K, expandable to 256 K.
Display: LCD displaying 4 lines of 80 characters each.
Physical: Weighed 9 pounds.
Production: In production by 1983.
Cost: $2995.

Value: $40-$100

GRiD Systems Compass Computer
Processor: Intel 8086.
RAM: 256 K, expandable to 0.5 M.
Display: 6-inch black-and-white electroluminescent screen.
Operator input: Keyboard with function keys.
Data storage: Had both an external 5.25-inch floppy drive and an external 10 M hard drive.
Physical: 15" L by 11.5" W by 2" H. Ran on 120V or on a battery pack.
Production: Introduced in early 1982.
Cost: $6000-8000.

This machine ran the MS-DOS operating system and the Compass Computer Operating System (CCOS). It used bubble-memory, and had both serial and parallel interfaces.

Value: $50-$125

Gavilan
Processor: Intel 8088.
RAM: 64 K, expandable to 128 K.
Display: LCD displaying 8 lines of 66 characters each.
Operator input: keyboard.
Data storage: Integral 320 K floppy drive.
Physical: 2.75" H by 11.4" W by 11.4" L. Weight was 9 pounds, or 14 pounds with the optional printer. It ran on rechargeable NiCad batteries.
Production: Introduced in 1983.
Cost: $3995.

This machine ran a proprietary operating system, and the MS-DOS operating system. It had an RS-232 serial interface and a touchpad "mouse". Distribution was to high-volume users, and through OEMs of software and hardware.

Value: $75-$150

HP (Hewlett-Packard) 110
Processor: Harris 80C86, running at 5.33 MHz.
RAM: 272 K CMOS.
Display: LCD displaying 16 lines of 80 characters each.
Operator input: Keyboard with eight function keys.
Data storage: A 710 K 3.5-inch floppy drive was optional, and there was a RAM-disk.
Physical: 13" by 10" by 3", weighed 9 pounds. Its rechargeable lead acid batteries were claimed to drive the machine for 20 hours.
Production: Introduced in 1984.
Cost: $2995.

The 110 ran version 2.01 of the MS-DOS operating system. It came with software in ROM, and it had an RS-232C serial port, a Hewlett-Packard Interface Loop (HPIL) port, and a modular phone jack for the internal modem.

Value: $100-$150

Tandy/Radio Shack TRS-80 Model 200
Production: Announced in 1985.

Value: $50-$100

Toshiba T-1100
Processor: Intel 8088.
Data storage: One 720 K floppy drive.
Production: Introduced in January of 1986, and was in production for about six months. A relatively small number were sold.

This machine was Toshiba's first laptop. It was the precurser of the very popular T-1100 Plus.

Value: $175-$275

Toshiba T-1100 Plus
Data storage: Two floppy drives.
Production: Introduced in mid-1986, and was in production for about a year.

This extremely popular machine helped launch the laptop market as we know it today.

Value: $125-$250

IBM Convertible PC, Courtesy of International Business Machines Corporation

IBM 5140 Convertible PC
Processor: 80C88.
RAM: 256 K, expandable to 512 K.
Display: Detachable non-backlit LCD display with 25 lines of 80 characters each, and a resolution of 640-by-200 pixels. It could also drive black-and-white or color monitors. (cont.)

5140 IBM cont.

Operator input: 78-key keyboard.
Data storage: Two 3.5-inch floppy disk drives.
Physical: 14.17" D by 12.19" W by 2.64" H, weighed 12.17 pounds. Used a battery pack.
Production: Introduced April 2, 1986.
Cost: Model 2 was $1695, and the Model 22 was $1675.

This machine was IBM's first laptop. It came with version 3.2 of the DOS operating system. It supersceeded IBM's 5155 Portable PC. The Model 2 came with more software than the Model 22. There was a 72-pin bus expansion on the back.

Value: $100-$200

Zenith Data Systems Z-181
Processor: Intel 8088.
Physical: About the same size as the Z-184 SupersPort.
Production: Introduced about 1986.

The Z-181 was Zenith's first laptop. It was also designated the ZFL-181.

Zenith Data Systems Z-184 SupersPort
Processor: Intel 8088.
RAM: 640 K, expandable to 1.6 M.
Display: 10.5-inch LCD CGA with a resolution of 640-by-200 pixels. An external RGB monitor was also available.
Operator input: 78-key keyboard. An external numeric keypad was also available.
Data storage: Two 3.5-inch 720 K floppy drives. An external 5.25-inch floppy drive was optional, as was a 20 M hard drive.
Physical: 12.2" by 12.2" by 3.1". Weighed 12.3 pounds. Had an external NiCad battery.
Production: In production by 1989.
Cost: $1999 with two floppy drives. $2799 with a 20 M hard drive and one floppy.

This very popular laptop could take either a 1200 or 2400 Baud internal modem. A case was optional.

Value: $200-350

Zenith Data Systems SupersPort 286
Processor: Intel 80286, running at 12MHz.
RAM: 1 M, expandable to 2 M.
Display: 10.5-inch backlit LCD CGA with 640-by-400 pixel resolution and eight greyscales. Could also drive an external RGB monitor.
Operator input: 79-key keyboard. An external numeric keypad was available.
Data storage: 3.5-inch, 1.44 M floppy-drive and 20 M hard-drive. An external floppy-drive was available.
Physical: 15.4" by 12.2" by 3.1". Weighed 14.6 pounds. The external NiCad battery weighed 4.1 pounds.
Production: In production by 1989.
Cost: $5499 with the 40 M hard drive, $4999 with the 20 M.

The 286 was an upgraded version of the popular SupersPort. An internal 2400 Baud modem was optional.

Value: $250-$450

Apple Mac Portable
Display: Active matrix screen.
Operator input: Keyboard and built-in trackball.
Physical: 16 pounds.
Production: Introduced in 1989.
Cost: About $6000.

This was the first Macintosh portable.

Value: $600-$1200

II-6.3. NOTEBOOKS

The next stage of portable evolution, the notebooks, came in 1981 with the Epson HX-20. Footprints of the early notebooks were typically the size of an 8.5-by-11-inch sheet of paper and their weights ranged from just under ten pounds down to around three pounds. There were sacrifices in functionality, however, most notably in the area of storage media. Files were often imported and exported by cable, and once in the notebooks, RAM was often the only form of storage. These early machines were clearly only auxiliaries to desk-top machines. However, with the introduction of the Compaq LTE and LTE 286, the notebooks developed into full-function computers. These 8.5-inch by 11.0-inch, 7.7-pound machines could be fitted with 20 and 40 Megabyte hard-drives in addition to their standard 1.44 Megabyte 3.5-inch floppy-disk drives, and ushered in notebooks that could serve as a user's only machine.

Epson HX-20
Processor: CMOS 6801.
RAM: 16 K.
Display: Displayed four lines of 20 characters each.
Operator input: Keyboard.
Data storage: Integral microcassette.
Physical: Weighed under three pounds.
Production: Introduced in 1981.

The HX-20 was considered by many to be the first true laptop computer. It contained a small printer.

Value: $100-$175

Tandy/Radio Shack TRS-80 Model 100
Processor: OKI 80C85, running at 2.4 MHz.
RAM: 8 K, expandable to 32 K.
Display: LCD displaying upper and lower case characters in 8 lines of 40 characters each.
Operator input: 56-key keyboard with 8 programmable function keys.
Data storage: Cassette
Physical: Dimensions were approximately 2" by 11.7" by 8.3", weighed less than four pounds. It ran on four AA batteries, supplying 5 V, but had a 110 V AC adaptor. Internal NiCad batteries were charged from the alkaline batteries.
Production: Introduced in 1983.
Cost: $799 to $1134 depending on the amount of memory.

This early notebook had both a parallel printer interface and an RS-232C serial interface. Several programs were stored in ROM. It had an integral modem. This machine was also sold by Kyocera, in a slightly different configuration, as the PC-8200.

Value: $25-$75

Teleram Model 4000
Processor: Zilog Z-80.
RAM: 64 K.
Display: LCD, displaying 8 lines.
Production: Introduced November of 1983.
Cost: $2495.

The Model 4000 ran CP/M.

Value: $25-$75

Teleram Model 5000
Processor: Zilog Z-80.
RAM: 64 K.
Display: LCD, displaying 16 lines.
Production: Introduced November of 1983.
Cost: $1995.

The Model 5000 ran CP/M.

Value: $25-$75

Convergent Technologies WorkSlate
Processor: Hitachi 6303.
RAM: 16 K.
Display: LCD display of 16 lines of 46 characters each.
Data storage: Microcassette with 60 K capacity.
Physical: Weighed a bit more than three pounds.
Production: In production by 1984.
Cost: $895

The WorkSlate incorporated, among other things, a spreadsheet function.
It used plug-in ROM modules to store programs.

Value: $20-$50

Micro-Office Systems Technology RoadRunner
Display: LCD, displaying 8 lines of 80 characters each.
Operator input: Standard-sized keyboard with 73 keys.
Data storage: Removable 32 K storage cartridges.
Physical: Weighed five pounds.
Production: In production by 1984.
Cost: $1895.

Value: $20-$50

NEC (Nippon Electric Co.) Portable
Production: In production by 1984.

NEC also made the TRS-80 Model 100.

Value: $25-$75

NEC (Nippon Electric Co.) UltraLight
RAM: 640 K nonexpandable.
Display: LCD CGA with 640-by-200 pixel resolution. 9.6-inch diagonal.
Operator input: 78-key keyboard.
Data storage: 1 M silicon disk.
Physical: The NiCad batteries were reported to give a two-hour running time. 11.8" by 8.3" by 1.4", weighed 4.4 pounds.
Production: Introduced in October of 1988.
Cost: $2499. A model with two meg of RAM was available for $2999.

The UltraLite was a pioneer in the notebook category, but it lacked the conventional storage (floppy and hard drives) found in its successors. A 2400-Baud modem was standard. It had both a serial port and a custom expansion port.

Value $250-$500

Zenith Data Systems MinisPort
RAM: 1 M, expandable to 2 M.
Display: 9.5-inch diagonal LCD CGA with resolution of 640-by-200 pixels. An external monitor was optional.
Operator input: 80-key keyboard.
Data storage: 2-inch 720 K floppy drive. External 5.25-inch and 3.5-inch floppy drives were optional.
Physical: 12.4" by 9.8" by 1.3". Weighed 5.9 pounds. Used NiCad batteries.
Production: Introduced in 1989.
Cost: $1999 for the 1 M model. $2799 for the 2 M model.

The MinisPort was unusual in its use of the 2-inch floppy drive. This data storage device never caught on. It had serial and parallel ports, and came with DOS and FastLynx. Options included a 1200 Baud modem and a case.

Value: $100-$200

Compaq LTE
RAM: 640 K, expandable to 1 M.
Display: LCD CGA with 640-by-200 pixels displayed on a 9-inch screen with four shades of grey.
Operator input: 80-key keyboard. A numeric keypad was also available.
Data storage: 1.44 M 3.5-inch floppy drive, with a 20 M hard-drive available as an option.
Physical: 11.0" by 8.5" by 1.9", and weighed 7.7 pounds. The rechargeable NiCad battery weighed 1.5 pounds.
Production: Introduced in October of 1989.
Cost: $2399, or $2999 with the hard-drive.

The LTE and LTE 286 were the first full-function notebook computers, including standard floppy and hard-drives. As such, they are historically-

important machines. Both had serial and parallel ports, and one proprietary expansion slot. A 2400-Baud modem was available as an option, as was a case, an external monitor, a keyboard, a separate keypad, a tap drive, and MS-DOS 4.0.

Value: $400-$800

Compaq LTE 286

RAM: 640 K, expandable to 2.6 M.
Display: LCD CGA with 640-by-200 pixels displayed on a 9-inch screen with four shades of grey.
Operator input: 80-key keyboard.
Data storage: 1.44 M 3.5-inch floppy drive, with 20 M and 40 M hard-drives available as an option.
Physical: 11.0" by 8.5" by 1.9", and weighed 7.7 pounds. The rechargeable NiCad battery weighed 1.5 pounds.
Production: Introduced in October of 1989.
Cost: $3999, $4799 with the 40 M hard drive.

The LTE and LTE 286 were the first full-function notebook computers, including standard floppy and hard-drives. As such, they are historically important machines. Both had serial and parallel ports, and one proprietary expansion slot. A 2400-Baud modem was available as an option, as was an external monitor, a keyboard, a separate keypad, MS-DOS 4.0, and a tape drive. In late 1990 this was possibly the most powerful notebook available.

Value: $600-$1200

Tandy/Radio Shack 1100FD
RAM: 640 K, expandable to 1.6 M.
Display: Backlit LCD CGA screen with resolution of 640-by-200 pixels.
Operator input: 84-key keyboard.
Data storage: 3.5-inch 720 K floppy drive.
Physical: 12.2" by 9.8" by 2.4". Weighed 6.2 pounds.
Production: Introduced about 1990.
Cost: $999.

The 1100FD was basically the same machine as the Panasonic 150B. It had a rechargeable, removeable lead-acid battery, and came standard with serial and parallel ports. Options included a 2400-Baud modem, an extra battery, a car adaptor and a carrying case. It had built-in DOS and Tandy's Deskmate. **Value: $200-$350**

Panasonic CF-150B
RAM: 640 K, expandable to 1.6 M.
Display: Backlit LCD CGA screen with a resolution of 640-by-200 pixels.
Operator input: 84-key keyboard.
Data storage: One 3.5-inch 720 K floppy drive.
Physical: 12.2" by 9.8" by 2.4". Weighed 6.2 pounds.
Production: Introduced about 1990.
Cost: $1149.

The 150B was basically the same machine as the Tandy 1100FD. It had a rechargeable, removeable lead-acid battery, and came standard with serial and parallel ports and a carrying case. Options included a 2400-Baud modem, an extra battery and a car adaptor. This machine represented a revival of the basic and inexpensive portable. **Value: $200-$350**

II-6-4. HANDHELDS

The smallest portables were the handhelds. These machines were nominally the size of pocket calculators. Their size was somewhat limited by the need for a screen and keyboard for user interface, although pen-based units alleviated this problem somewhat. Easily held in one hand, and with weights ranging down to about a pound, they were comparable in size to the pocket calculators they were closely related to. However, as was the case with the notebooks before the introduction of the Compaq LTE series, the handhelds served only as auxiliary machines to larger machines due to their lack of standard storage media.

Courtesy of Tandy Corporation

Tandy/Radio Shack TRS-80 Pocket Computer
RAM: 1.9 K.
Display: LCD displaying 1 line of 24 characters.
Operator input: 53-key keyboard with numeric keypad.
Data storage: Cassette.
Physical: Ran on four mercury batteries.
Production: Introduced in 1980.
Cost: Introductory price was $229.

The PC-1 was manufactured by Sharp, and was the first battery-powered computer sold in the U.S.
  Value: $50-$150 for PC-1, $25-$100 for PC-2 and PC-3.

Quasar Data Products HHC (Hand-Held Computer)
RAM: 2 K, expandable to 4 K.
Display: LCD, displaying 1 line of 26 characters. It could also drive a color TV with a display of 16 lines of 32 characters each.
Operator input: 65-key keyboard, with three programmable function keys.
Data storage: Cassette.
Physical: 8.94" by 1.19" by 3.75", weighed 14 ounces. It used NiCad batteries.
Production: Introduced in June of 1980.

This machine was basically the same as the Panasonic HHC, which was produced by Matsushita, the parent company.

Value: $25-$75

Panasonic RL-H1000 HHC (Hand Held Computer)
Processor: 6502, running at 1 MHz.
RAM: 2 K, expandable to 4 K.
Display: LCD, displaying 1 line of 24 characters. It could also drive a color TV with a display of 16 lines of 32 characters each.
Operator input: 65-key keyboard.
Data storage: Cassette and ROM cartridges.
Physical: 8.94" by 1.19" by 3.75", weighed 14 ounces. It used NiCad batteries.
Production: Introduced in June of 1980.

This machine was basically the same as the Quasar HHC, which was produced by Matsushita, the parent company. It was known as "The Link".

Value: $25-$75

Sharp PC-1500
Data storage: A cassette interface was available.
Physical: Could run from AC power as well as rechargeable batteries.
Production: Introduced in 1982.

The 1500 had a four-color plotter and printer.

Value: $20-$60

Sharp PC-5000
Processor: 8088.
RAM: 128 K, expandable to 256 K.
Display: LCD, displaying 8 lines of 80 characters each.
Data storage: Cassette available.
Production: Introduced in May of 1983.
Cost: $1995 for the basic system, $2750 for the complete system.

The PC-5000 ran MS-DOS, and could be bought with an integral printer for an additional $395.

Value: $20-$60

HP (Hewlett-Packard) 75 Portable Computer
RAM: 16 K, expandable to 24 K.
Display: Liquid crystal display could display 32 5-by-8 pixel dot-matrix characters.
Operator input: Integral QWERTY keyboard.
Data storage: Had a built-in magnetic-card reader with a capacity of 1.3 K. Cassette drive available as an option.
Physical: 10" by 5" by 1.25", weighed 26 ounces.
Production: In production by June of 1983.

An acoustic modem and a printer were available as peripherals.

Value: $25-$75

Xerox 1810
Processor: NSC800.
RAM: 80 K.
Display: LCD, displaying 3 80-character lines. Could also drive a TV.
Data storage: Microcassette. The Xerox 1845 5.25-inch floppy-drive expansion unit was also available for $1195.
Physical: Weighed five pounds.
Production: Introduced on October 12, 1983.
Cost: $2195

The 1810 used ROM cartridges to store software.

Value: $20-$60

HP (Hewlett-Packard) 71B Computer
Processor: Custom 4-bit processor.
RAM: 4 K.
Display: One-line LCD display displayed 22 characters.
Operator input: QWERTY keyboard.
Physical: 3 7/8" by 7 1/2" by 1", weighed 12 ounces.
Production: In production by July of 1984.

The 71B contained BASIC.

Value: $20-$60

TI (Texas Instruments) CC-40 (Compact Computer 40)
Processor: TMS-70C20.
RAM: 6 K, expandable to 16 K.
Display: LCD displaying single line of 31 characters.
Operator input: 65-key keyboard.
Physical: Battery powered.
Production: In production by 1984.
Cost: $249.95

The CC-40 could read from cartridges or a waferdrive tape. It could be programmed in BASIC.

Value: $20-$60

Poquet PC
RAM: 512 K.
Display: CGA LCD displaying 640-by-200 pixels on a 7.2-inch diagonal screen.
Operator input: 77-key keyboard.
Data storage: 640 K ROM storage cards. An external 1.44 M 3.5-inch floppy drive was also available.
Physical: 8.8" by 4.3" by 0.93", weighed 1 pound. It ran on two AA alkaline batteries, that were replaced when depleted.
Production: Introduced late in 1989.
Cost: $1995

This machine had version 3.3 of the MS-DOS operating system in ROM. It had a custom expansion port, and a serial port. It could run 100 hours on AA batteries, and was MS-DOS compatible.

Value: $350-$500

GRiD Systems GRiDPad
RAM: 1 M RAM, nonexpandable.
Display: LCD, 640-by-400 pixel, 10-inch diagonal.
Operator input: Pen input. Also had an external keyboard port.
Data storage: 128 K or 256 K RAM cards. Floppy drive and 20 M hard-drive expansion units were available.
Physical: 12.4" by 9.3" by 1.4", weighed 4.5 pounds. Had rechargeable NiCad batteries.
Production: Announced in 1989.
Cost: $2370.

This machine could recognize handwriting made with the input pen.

Value: $50-$100

HP (Hewlett-Packard) 95LX
Production: Was introduced about May of 1991.
Cost: $700

Value: $300-$400

III. ACCESSORIES AND PERIPHERALS

The peripherals for personal computers developed along with the computers themselves. They included input and output devices, data-storage devices, memory, communications equipment, and others. Some of these devices had been in production before there were personal computers. The Teletypes and dumb terminals used to interface with many early microcomputers, as well as the 8-inch floppy drives used to store data, were adapted from the mainframe and minicomputer industries. Other devices came from industries completely unrelated to computers. Audio cassette tape recorders were used for data storage, most early CRT displays were television sets, and many early printers were adapted from typewriters and cash-register receipt printers.

Peripherals were hardly optional for the earliest machines. While most of the early S-100 kits could be operated using their toggle-switches as input and their rows of LEDs for output, this was extremely awkward and limited the usefulness of the machine. Devices such as tape readers (magnetic or paper) allowed the operator to avoid tedious re-entry of code each time the computer was turned on, and Teletypes or CRTs allowed practical interaction with the machine. While this close relationship between personal computers and their peripherals was most pronounced in the earliest kit machines, it remains to the present day. Most modern computers are used with some peripheral, whether it is a mouse, a modem, a joystick, a sound board, or a printer.

The peripherals are grouped here by type. As with the listing of the computers in Chapter One, they appear in each section approximately in the order in which they were introduced. However, in many cases products were introduced earlier than the date given. Unless the dates are specifically stated to be introduction dates, the machines may have been in production significantly earlier.

III-1. PAPER TAPE STORAGE:

One of the earliest forms of off-line data storage for personal computers were the paper tape readers and writers. Their principle of operation was similar to the punch cards previously used in mainframes, in that the presence or absence of a hole indicated the status of a bit. In the case of paper tape, however, the media was a continuous strip, as opposed to the individual cards read by card readers.

Paper tape was one of the standard media used to store and distribute programs, and it was often simply pulled through the readers by hand. While the data density was not high, nor the data rate fast, it was a durable and relatively permanent form of storage.

Teleterminal Fly Teleterminal Reader 30
Type: Paper tape reader.
Speed: 0-310 cps, bidirectional.
Production: In production by November of 1975.
Cost: $295 as a kit, $365 assembled.

The Fly read one-inch, eight-level paper tape. It was compatible with Altair 8800 parallel interface board.

Value: $200-$300

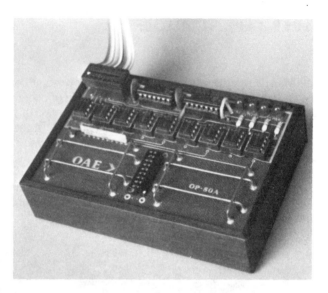

Oliver Audio Engineering (OAE) OP-80A
Type: Paper tape reader.
Speed: Advertisements claimed "No moving parts. Reads paper tape as fast as you can pull it through!" 5000 CPS was the limit of the electronics.
Interface: 8-bit parallel.
Physical: The OP-80A's dimensions were 4.6" by 3.2" by 1.0", and it weighed less than one pound. It was housed in an anodized aluminum box and had four status LEDs.
Production: In production by April of 1976.
Cost: $74.50 as a kit, $95.00 assembled.

This reader had no moving parts, the paper tape was pulled through by hand. A 12 K BASIC could be loaded in 30 seconds "by experienced tape pullers."

Value: $200-$300

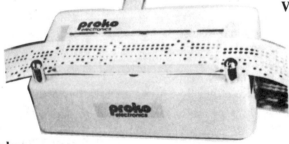

Proko
Type: Paper tape reader.
Interface: Parallel.
Production: In production by February of 1977.

(cont.)

Proko cont.
Cost: $42 as a kit, $55 assembled.

The Proko read nine-level paper tape. Light had to be externally supplied, and the tape was pulled by hand.

Value: $200-$300.

Heath Data Systems H10 paper tape reader punch unit
Type: Paper tape reader and writer.
Speed: Could read at 50 characters per second, and write at 10 characters per second.
Interface: Parallel.
Physical: Weighed 29 pounds.
Production: Introduced about August of 1977.
Cost: $350.

This machine was sold as a kit, and was "Heath's principal mass storage unit for use with the H11 product line." It could also be used with the H8. It had a built-in power supply and a stepper motor drive, and was "Styled to match the H8 and H11 computers." It used a one-inch wide paper roll or eight-level fanfold. A paper-roll holder was available as an option, as was a chad collector tray and collector box for the outputted fan-fold tape. Paper tape was available in eight-inch rolls (900 feet) at $10 for three, and three boxes of fan-fold tape (approximately 1000 feet each) were $10.

Value: $150-$250.

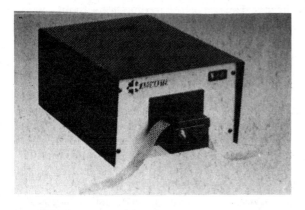

Addmaster 612
Speed: 150 cps, 50 to 9600 Baud.
Interface: RS-232C, parallel or current-loop.
Physical: Available in rack-mounted or desktop models.
Production: In production by May of 1979.

The 612 used X-on and X-off or manual control, and read 5-8 level tape with 7-11 frames per character. It used even or odd parity.

Value: $200-$300

Tandy/Radio Shack TRS-80 CR-510
Type: Connected card reader.
Speed: Read 150 cards per minute.
Cost: $1595.

The CR-510 used reflected light to sense holes.

Value: $150-$200

III-2. MAGNETIC STORAGE:

Magnetic tape drives were the first popular form of magnetic storage media to be used with personal computers. Inexpensive audio cassette recorders offered readily-available bulk data storage for the new personal computer industry. One of their liabilities was the linear access of the data on the tape. Magnetic floppy disks could access data randomly distributed on the media much more rapidly than tapes. While floppy drives had previously been used only in the minicomputer and mainframe machines, they began to be adapted to personal computers. Prices fell as sales volumes rose, and soon floppy drives became the standard storage device, rendering cassette tape drives obsolete. In their turn, hard drives, with their much larger storage capacities and faster access times, displaced floppy drives as the main bulk storage devices. Today a personal computer without a hard disk drive is a rarity.

III-2-1. MAGNETIC TAPE STORAGE:

Magnetic tape storage, having its origins in the large magnetic tape reels used on mainframes, was a more convenient and dense storage media than paper tape. Further, it was readily and cheaply accessible to the early personal computer user in the form of audio cassette tape players. While some of these were sold specifically as data storage devices, they were basically the same units that could be bought in any appliance store.

As the floppy disk drives became more popular and inexpensive, the slow speeed of the audio tape systems made them less appealing. Data must be accessed linearly on a tape; the heads cannot jump to other sections of the media as they can on a disk. Today only specialized forms of tape cassettes, used to back-up hard disk drives, are still marketed to microcomputer users.

Southwest Development Company Bulk Memory Microcomputer Audio Cassette Interface
Type: Cassette.
Speed: Variable Baud rate, set at 300 Baud for use with inexpensive audio cassette recorder.

Interface: Standard TTY.
Production: In production by January of 1976.
Cost: $83.50.

Value: $125-$175

National Multiplex Computer Aid Digital Data Recorder
Type: Cassette.
Speed: Up to 2400 Baud, could load 8 K in 34 seconds.
Production: In production by January of 1976.
Cost: $149.95.

This machine came with prerecorded 8080 test software.

Value: $25-$75

National Multiplex Computer Aid 3M1
Type: Cassette.
Speed: Nominal tape speed was 5 inches per second. Data transfer was at 4800 Baud.
Production: In production by December of 1976.
Cost: $169.95

The 3M1 used DC100A 3M data cartridges containing 150 feet of 0.150 tape.

Value: $25-$75

National Multiplex Computer Aid 3M3
Type: Cassette.
Speed: Nominal tape speed was 8-inches per second. Data transfer was at 9600 Baud.
Cost: $189.95.

The 3M3 used DC300 3M data cartridges containing 300 feet of tape.
Value: $25-$75

Data Dek DD-100
Type: Cassette.
Production: In production by April of 1976.

This machine had remote control of all functions and photo-cell sensing of end-of-tape and data block.
Value: $25-$75

Economy Company
Type: Cassette.
Production: In production by April of 1976.
Cost: Approximately $100.

This was a variable-speed cassette deck.
Value: $25-$75

The Digital Group PHI-F and PHI-1 Cassette Storage System
Type: Cassette.
Speed: 800 bytes per second, had 100-inch-per-second search speed, and 5-inch-per-second tape speed.
Interface: 8-bit parallel.
Production: In production by July of 1976.
Cost: PHI-F interface kit was $135, PHI-1 assembled drive was $115.

These systems could control 1 to 4 Phi-Deck cassette transports.
Value: $40-$75

SWTPC (Southwest Technical Products Corp.) AC-30 Cassette Interface
Type: Cassette.
Speed: 300 Baud.
Interface: RS-232 serial interface.
Physical: 12¾" by 3" by 12½" aluminum chassis.
Production: In production by July of 1976.
Cost: $79.50.

The AC-30 had independent control circuits for two cassettes.
Value: $50-$75

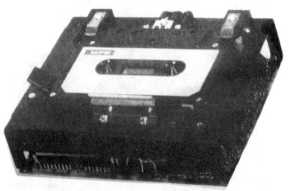

MFE 250B Digital Tape Transport
Type: Cassette.
Capacity: Up to 800 bpi.
Speed: 320 Kbps data transfer.
Interface: 8-bit parallel interface available.
Physical: 4.39" by 5.46" by 2.42".
Production: In production by November of 1976.
Cost: $525.

A 15,000 hour MTBF was claimed for the 250B. **Value: $50-$75**

Realistic CTR-40
Type: Cassette.
Value: $25-$75

Tandy/Radio-Shack TRS-80
Computer Cassette Recorder
Type: Cassette.
Value: $50-$75

216

Economy Company Triple I Phi-Deck Super Deck
Type: Cassette.
Physical: Had a die-cast frame, but no cover.
Production: In production by January of 1977.

This was a remote controlled, variable-speed cassette drive.
Value: $50-$75

PerCom Data Company CIS-30 +
Type: Cassette.
Speed: 120 bytes per second.
Production: In production by February of 1977.
Cost: $69.95 as a kit, $89.95 assembled.

The CIS-30+ was a cassette I/O for the SWTP 6800 that ran an ordinary cassette recorder. **Value: $40-$75**

Techtran 4100 cassette recorder
Type: Cassette.
Interface: RS-232.
Production: In production by March of 1977.
Cost: $595.
Value: $25-$50

Sykes Compucorder 100
Type: Cassette.
Capacity: 3.5 Mbit storage.
Speed: 500 characters/second.
Production: In production by March of 1977.
Cost: $950.
Value: $25-$50

Amilon A9 Cassette Transport
Type: Cassette.
Production: In production by March of 1977.

The A9 was similar to the A7, but with a different head mount and an index counter. **Value: $25-$50**

Wollensak 9576 and 9677
Type: Cassette.

The 9577 had an optional end-of-tape sensor.

Value: $25-$50

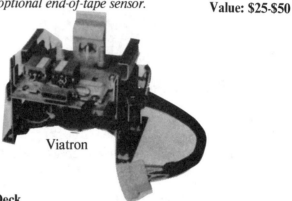

Viatron

Viatron Cassette Deck
Type: Cassette.
Production: In production by September of 1977.
Cost: Computer cassette deck alone was available for $35, amplifiers and control boards were available for $40.

Value: $40-$75

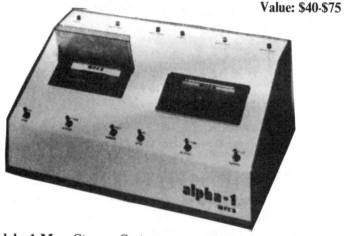

MECA alpha-1 Mass Storage System
Type: Cassette.
Capacity: Over 500 K bytes per side on a C-60 tape.
Speed: Data rate was 780 bytes per second, and average file-access time was 17 seconds. Could load 8 K of data in less than 11 seconds using a 6250 Baud rate.
Interface: Through the S-100 bus.
Production: Introduced about January of 1978.
Cost: Prices began at $240. Units that were plug-compatible with the TRS-80 had prices starting at $399.

(cont.)

MECA cont.

This device was offered in two versions: for S-100 computers (which could control up to 4 drives), or as a stand-alone cassette operating system with extended BASIC. The dual cassette system included the MCOS operating system, with extended BASIC.

Value: $50-$75

Techtran 815 Datacassette
Type: Cassette.
Speed: The interface could run at 110 or 320 bps.
Interface: RS-232C.
Physical: Weight was six pounds for the standard version, 10 pounds for the battery-powered version.
Production: Introduced about January of 1978.
Cost: $950, or $1095 for battery-powered version.

Value: $50-$75

CC-8.

Computer Aid CC-8 Digital Data Recorder
Type: Cassette.
Speed: This asynchronous recorder could be used from 110 to 4800 Baud.
Interface: RS-232 or TTL.
Production: In production by January of 1978.
Cost: $175.

Advertisements for the CC-8 claimed it was "Used by major computer manufacturers, Bell Telephone and U.S. Government for program reloading and field servicing."

Value: $25-$50

Panasonic RQ-309DS
Type: Cassette.
Physical: Portable cassette recorder in black plastic case and aluminum trim.
Production: In production by July of 1978.
Cost: $25-$75

This recorder was used with various personal computers of its era, e.g. the OSI Challenger series.

Value: $25-$50

MECA beta-1.
Type: Cassette.
Capacity: 1 Mby.
Speed: The tape speed was greater than 100 in per second, and access times were typically 10 seconds or less. "Fast load" loaded at 8000 bps.
Interface: Operated from an 8-bit parallel port, but a serial interface was available that doubled the loading speed (to 16 K bps).
Production: In production by December of 1978.
Cost: $399 assembled, no kits were available.

The beta-1 was not aimed at S-100 computers. It had an 8035 microprocessor.
Value: $25-$50

Commodore PET C2N
Type: Cassette.
Production: Introduced about April of 1979.
Cost: $100
This was a second tape drive for the PET.

Value: $25-$50

III-2-2. FLOPPY-DISK STORAGE:

The floppy disk, developed in the late 1960s by IBM, replaced magnetic tape as the standard bulk-storage media for personal computers. Its main advantages over tape were ease of handling the storage media and fast access time. At first many microcomputer systems used the IBM 3740 format for their floppies. By 1983, 5.25-inch minifloppy disk capacitites from several companies were well above 1 megabyte, with some over 3 megabytes. These formats were propriety, however, and drives were expensive (in the neighborhood of $500). Standardized formats for the 5.25-inch floppy disk were established with the introduction of the IBM PC in 1981.

In 1980 the 3.5-inch microfloppy was introduced by Sony. Unlike earlier floppies, which were housed in flexable sheaths, this floppy disk was housed in a hard plastic case with a sliding metal shutter. Initially having a capacity of 437 kilobytes, this small-format disk came to be the industry standard, with capacities ranging up to 2.8 megabytes.

Helios
Type: 8-inch floppy disk drive.
This drive was often used with the Proc Tech computers.

Value: $50-$100

Innovex
Type: 8-inch floppy disk drive.
Production: In production by June of 1976.
Cost: This drive was sold for half price, $500, at a June 1976 show.

Value: $50-$100

Sykes Datatroncis Floppy Drive Kit
Type: Floppy disk drive.
Capacity: 630 K bytes per diskette in dual-density format mode, or 256 K in IBM-compatible format mode.
Interface: 8-bit parallel.
Production: In production by August of 1976.
Cost: $1398 as a kit.

Value: $50-$100

ICOM Microperipherals Frugal Floppy
Type: Floppy disk drive.
Interface: Came with interface cable and IBM-compatible controller.
Production: In production by August of 1976.
Cost: $1195, or $995 "in small OEM quantities."

The Frugal Floppy came with FDOS-II software.

Value: $50-$100

Early FD-8

Later FD-8

MSI (Midwest Scientific Instruments) FD-8 System
Type: Floppy disk drive.
Interface: One 8-bit bidirectional data port.
Physical: This machine had its own cabinet and power supply.
Production: In production by September of 1976.
Cost: $1150 as a kit, $1395 wired and tested.

The FD-8 had a 3 K RAM buffer. **Value: $50-$100**

IMSAI (IMS Associates, Inc.)
Type: Floppy disk drive.
Capacity: 243 K bytes using IBM 3740 format.
Physical: Came in a cabinet with a power supply.
Production: In production by September of 1976.
Cost: Drive and controller were $1449 as a kit, $1649 assembled.

This drive was compatible with the IMSAI 8080.

Value: $100-$150

PerCom Data Company Li'l Floppy
Type: 5.25-inch floppy disk drive.
Capacity: 110 K.
Speed: Loaded 12 K in 2 seconds.
Interface: Altair/IMSAI interface, (S-100).
Physical: In production by December of 1976.
Cost: $695 as a kit, $810 assembled.

The Li'l Floppy was for Altair/IMSAI and SWTP 6800.

Value: $75-$100

Shugart Associates Minifloppy drive SA-400
Type: 5.25-inch floppy disk drive.
Capacity: 89.6 K.
Speed: 125 K bute per second.
Physical: 3.25" high by 5.75" wide by 8.0" long, weighed 3 pounds.
Production: Introduced about December of 1976.
Cost: $390.

This machine was belt-driven by a DC motor. Shugart was one of the first floppy-disk-drive manufacturers, and this unit used the then-new 5.25" minidiskette (either the SA104 soft-sectored version or the SA105 hard-sectored unit).   **Value: $75-$125**

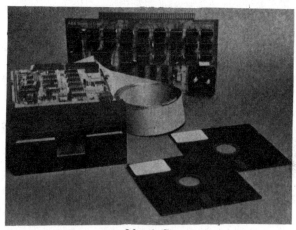

North Star

North Star Floppy Disk System
Type: 5.25-inch floppy disk drive.
Capacity: 90 K.
Interface: Interfaced through an S-100 card.
Production: Introduced about January of 1977.
Cost: $599 as a kit, $699 assembled.

This micro-disk system was for the Altair/IMSAI. The diskettes cost $4.50 each.   **Value: $50-$100**

SWTPC (Southwest Technical Products Corp.) FD-8 Disk Memory
Type: 8-inch floppy disk drive.
Production: In production by January of 1977.
Cost: $950 as a kit, $1195 assembled.

Value: $50-$100

MITS (Micro Instrumentation and Telemetry Systems) Altair Floppy Disk Drive
Type: Floppy disk drive.
Production: In production by October of 1975 ___ **Value:** $200-$300

Peripheral Vision
8-inch drive.

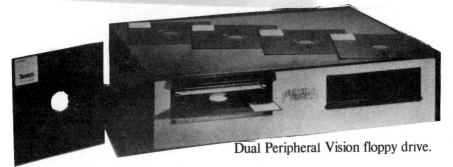

Dual Peripheral Vision floppy drive.

Peripheral Vision
Type: 8-inch floppy disk drive.
Physical: Blue cabinet available for $85.
Production: Introduced around February of 1977.
Cost: $750 as a kit, $850 assembled.

(cont.)

225

Peripheral Vision Cont.

This S-100-compatible drive had a bootstrap EPROM to operate with "no more toggling or paper tape." The drive was from Innovex. One interface card could support four floppies. A + 24V, 2A power supply was available for $45 as a kit or $65 assembled.

Value: $50-$100

iCOM Microperipherals iCOM Microfloppy
Type: Floppy disk drive.
Production: In production by March of 1977.

Value: $25-$75

Micropolis Meta Floppy
Type: 5.25-inch floppy disk drive.
Production: Introduced in 1977.

Value: $40-$100

Smoke Signal Broadcasting BFD-68 Basic Floppy Disk System
Type: Floppy disk drive.
Production: In production by July of 1977.
Cost: BFD-68 was $795, BFD-68-2 was $1169, and BFD-68-3 was $1539.

This system came assembled with a disk controller, and used the standard SS-50 bus of the SWTPC 6800. The cabinet and power supply could handle up to three Shugart Mini-Floppy Drives. The BFD-68 came with one drive, and the BFD-68-2 and BFD-68-3 came with two and three drives, respectively, They had a bootstrap PROM to initiate the DOS.

Value: $25-$75

Synetic Designs Co FDS-2
Type: Floppy disk drive.
Production: In production by July of 1977.

This drive used iCOM standard floppy disk drives. It used IBM 3540 and 3740 formats.

Value: $25-$50

227

Calcomp

Calcomp Computer Products 140/142/142M
Type: Floppy disk drive.
Interface: Through LSI-11, RS-232-C, and S-100 (all had a 50-pin LSI interface).
Physical: The 1149M cabinet assembly was available as an option.
Production: In production by August of 1977, when an advertisement stated that 50,000 drives had been delivered.

All of these drives were double-density, and one-or-two-sided types were available. The 143M drive (called "new" in August of 1977) was for two-sided, single or double density recording.

Value: $25-$50

SWTPC (Southwest Technical Products Corp.) MF-68 Dual Minifloppy
Type: 5.25-inch floppy disk drive.
Production: In production by August of 1977.
Cost: $995 as a kit.

This floppy drive was advertised for the SWTPC computer. It consisted of a kit with controller, chassis, cover, power supply, two Shugart drives, Floppy Disk Operating System (FDOS) and BASIC on a disk. Expansion to four drives was available in the MF-6X kit.

Value: $40-$100

MPI (Micro Peripherals, Inc.) Flexible Disk Series B51
Type: 5.25-inch floppy disk drive.
Capacity: Could store up to 250 K bytes in a double-density mode.
Physical: 3.25" by 5.55" by 8.0", weighed 3 pounds.
Production: In production by October of 1977.
Cost: $320. An S-100 controller was available for $299.

This device had a 5.25-inch band-driven head positioner.
Value: $25-$50

Vista Computer V80 Floppy Disk System
Type: 5.25-inch floppy disk drive.
Interface: S-100 controller.
Production: In production by January of 1978.
Cost: $649 as a kit, $749 assembled. Extra drives alone were $399 each. A TRS-80 version was available for $395.

This device was advertised for use with 8080 or Z-80 machines. Its S-100 compatible controller could control up to four drives, and it came with the VOS disk operating system.

Value: $25-$50

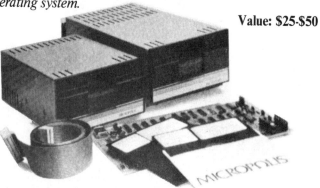

Micropolis MacroFloppy :1041 and :1042
Type: 5.25-inch floppy disk drive.
Capacity: 143 K.

Production: In production by February of 1978.
Cost: $695 for the :1041 and $795 for the :1042.

These drives were advertised for S-100/8080/Z-80 machines. The :1042 was the same as the :1041, but with regulators, a power supply, and a cover.
Value: $25-$50

MetaFloppy

Micropolis MetaFloppy :1054
Type: 5.25-inch floppy drive.
Capacity: Used 77 tracks instead of the usual 35 to give "more than four times the capacity of anyone else's 5.25-inch floppy."
Production: Introduced about February of 1978

The :1054 was advertised for use with S-100/8080/Z-80 machines. It included four drives in two dual configurations.
Value: $25-$50

Extensys FOS100 Floppy Disk System
Type: Floppy disk drive.
Speed: Average seek time was 33 milliseconds.
Interface: A file I/O board with an 8080A, 1 K of PROM, and 8 K of RAM.
Production: In production by April of 1978.

*This device used a PerSci controller board and two PerSci 277 floppy disk
drives. It used IBM-compatible format. The software was Extensys
Multiprocessor Operating System (EMOS).*

Value: $25-$50

299 open

232

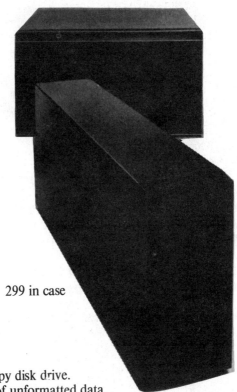

299 in case

PerSci 299
Type: Dual 8-inch floppy disk drive.
Capacity: 3.2M bytes of unformatted data.
Speed: 33 ms seek time (including settle).
Physical: 4.38" by 8.72" by 15.4".
Production: In production by June of 1978.

This was a dual-disk drive for double-sided data storage in various formats, including the IBM 3740 single-density format or the IBM 2D double-density format. It had write-protect capabilities.

Value: $25-$80

SWTPC (Southwest Technical Products Corp.) DMAF1
Type: Dual 8-inch floppy disk drive.
Capacity: About 600 K on single-density, double-sided disks.
Interface: This unit included an SS-50 bus compatible controller, that could handle four drives.
Physical: 5.4" by 17.1" by 20.5"
Production: Introduced about June of 1978.
Cost: $2000 as a kit, $2095 assembled.

The DMAF1 was available in kit or assembled form.

Value: $25-$50

233

Heath Data Systems WH17
Type: 5.25-inch minifloppy disk drive for Heathkit H8 system.
Capacity: 102 K.
Speed: Had a typical access time of less than 350 ms.
Physical: Integrated unit in a Heathkit-style box.
Production: Planned introduction was June of 1978.
Cost: $975.

The WH17 used a model 82 WANGCO drive, and standard hard-sectored 40-track diskettes with 10 sectors/track.

Value: $50-$100

Heath Data Systems H27 and WH27
Type: Dual floppy disk drive.
Physical: External dual floppy disk drive.
Production: In production by July of 1978.
Cost: $2595.

Advertisements claimed the "WH27's disk operating system was developed in conjunction with DEC and supports BASIC, FORTRAN and Assembly Languages...all available from Heath Data Systems Dealers."

Value: $50-$100

234

Tandy/Radio Shack
Type: 5.25-inch floppy disk drive.
Production: Announced in 1978.

Value: $25-$50

PerCom Data Company LFD-400
Type: Floppy disk drive.
Interface: The controller card plugged into the SS-50 bus.
Physical: Contained in a metal housing.
Production: In production by July of 1978.
Cost: $599.95

This device was sold assembled and tested. It used a Shugart SA 400 floppy-disk drive, and came with a power supply and controller. It came with two disks, one including SWTP 8 K BASIC and TSC editor and assembler.
Value: $25-$50

Innotronics
Type: Floppy disk drive.
Production: In production by August of 1978.

This company also made the Innovex Diskette and drive circa 1970.
Value: $25-$75

DB8/4

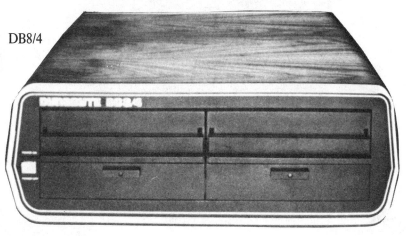

Dynabyte DB8/4
Type: Floppy disk drive.
Production: In production by October of 1978

Value: $25-$75

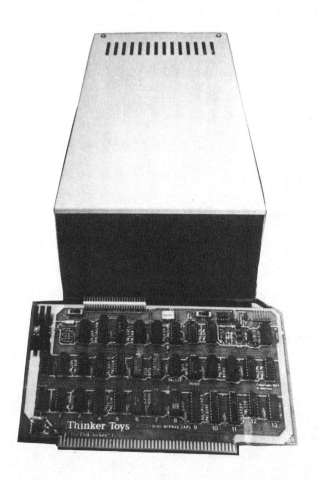

Thinker Toys Discus I
Type: 8-inch floppy disk drive.
Interface: Serial
Production: Available by November of 1978.
Cost: $995

This drive came assembled with all software. It ran on the S-100 bus, and was available with CP/M (for $70), MicroSoft BASIC (for $199) and MicroSoft FORTRAN (for $349).

Value: $50-$100

Vista Computer V200 Minifloppy Vista Disk System
Type: 5.25-inch floppy disk drive.
Capacity: Over 204 K.
Production: In production by January of 1979.
Cost: $699.

The V200 operated with Z-80 or 8080 systems with 24 K of RAM or more.
Value: $20-$40

Vista Computer V1000 Minifloppy Vista Disk System
Type: 8-inch floppy disk drive.
Capacity: 2000 K in IBM-compatible format.
Physical: Came in a "new, compact case."
Production: In production by January of 1979.
Cost: $2699.

The V1000 operated with Z-80 or 8080 systems with 24 K of RAM or more.
Value: $20-$40

Quay 80 F1
Type: 5.25-inch floppy disk drive
Capacity: 125 K.
Production: Introduced about February of 1979.
Cost: $795.

This S-100 system included the Q/80 FC cabinet and Q/80 FDC floppy-disk controller, the Q/FD1 band-driven floppy disk drive, and the QDOS operating system.
Value: $20-$50

Disk II

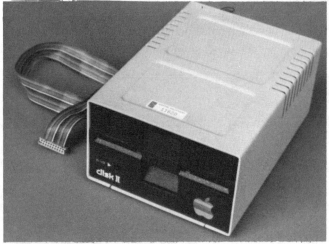

Apple Disk II
Type: 5.25-inch floppy disk drive.
Capacity: 116 K.

(cont.)

Apple Disk Cont.

Production: Introduced in June of 1978. The initial production rate was 30 per day.

Cost: $495.

The Disk II could be driven by the power supply of the Apple II. It came with a controller card and disk operating system software that gave "dynamic disk space allocation" which allowed the operator to store or retrieve a file on the disk without having to know the size of the file or its storage location on the disk. **Value: $75-$150**

Intronics 3400F

Intronics 3400 Sub-System

Capacity: Intronics 8-inch 410 and 420 floppy drives.

Production: In production by April of 1979.

Available in rack-mounted form or desk-top models with cherry and walnut cases. **Value: $20-$50**

Smoke Signal Broadcasting   Chieftan

Type: Floppy disk drive.

(cont.)

Chieftain (cont.)
Production: In production by April of 1979.   **Value: $20-$50**

2040, labeled "PET"

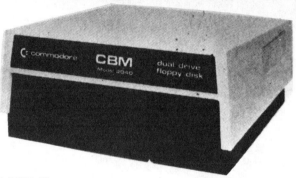

2040, labeled "CBM"

Commodore PET 2040 (2041)
Type: Dual (2040) or single (2041) floppy disk drive.
Capacity: 171.5 K per disk.
Interface: IEEE interface.
Production: In production by April of 1979.
Cost: $595 for single drive, $1095 for dual drive.

This drive used a 6504 processor and had 4 K for RAM. It could use single or dual sided diskettes.

    Value: $50-$75

Early 1541

Late 1541

Commodore PET 1540 (1541)
Type: Dual (1540) or single (1541) floppy disk drive.

Value: $25-$50

Several Lobo storage systems. The 5.25-inch drive is on the upper right, the dual 8-inch drive is on the bottom, and the hard-drive is the dark unit on the upper left.

Lobo
Type: 5.25-inch floppy disk drive.
Capacity: In production by November of 1979.

This was a single-sided minifloppy drive in a single-drive housing. It was advertised for the TRS-80.

Value: $25-$50

Lobo
Type: 8-inch floppy disk drive
Capacity: Up to 2.5 Mby total.
Production: In production by November of 1979.

This was a dual double or single-sided 8-inch floppy drive. It was advertised for the TRS-80.

Value: $50-$100

III-2-3. HARD-DISK STORAGE:

Hard disks allowed a great increase in storage capacity and access speed over floppy disks. The first hard disks affordable to the hobbyist had capacities in the 5 and 10 megabyte range. Initially a mainframe technology, at the time they became available for microcomputers they were still known as "Winchester" drives. This name seemingly originated from their development at IBM, and while various stories recount its origin, all apparently derive from the famous Winchester 30-30 rifle. In one story, the hard drive was being developed under the model number 3030, hence the association with "Winchester." In another, the 30-30 designation came about because one of the early drives had 30 Mby of fixed storage (where the media was not removable) and 30 Mby of removable-media storage. Regardless of its origin, the name is not in use today.

As with the floppy disk drives, hard drives first appeared in microcomputers in 8-inch and 5.25-inch formats. Later 3.5-inch and smaller formats appeared.

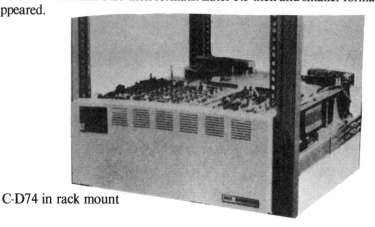

C-D74 in rack mount

OSI (Ohio Scientific Instruments) C-D74
Type: Hard-disk drive.
Capacity: 74 Mby.
Speed: 7.3 Mby per second, average access time was 34 ms.
Production: In production by October of 1977.
Cost: About $6000, including the OS-74 operating system.
This early hard-drive was advertised for use with personal computer. It was advertised as "quite possibly the world's highest performance data storage device," with "an unbelievable 34 milli-second average access time." It had 12 tracks per cylinder.

Value: $150-$250

Shugart Associates SA-1000
Type: Hard-disk drive.
Capacity: 5 or 10 Mby.
Cost: $1950.

Value: $100-$250

Sugart Associates SA-4000
Type: Hard-disk drive
Capacity: Available in 14.5 and 29 Mby capacities.
Interface: Could be controlled by the SA4600 controller (or others).
Physical: Weighed 35 pounds and was designed to fit in a standard 19-inch equipment rack.
Production: Introduced about June of 1978.
Cost: $2550 for the 14.5 Mby unit, $3550 for the 29 Mby unit.
The SA-4000 was described as "a unit that may have a major impact on the personal computer market a year or so from now" in the June 1978 issue of Byte.

Value: $100-$250

IMI
Type: 8-inch hard-disk drive.
Production: First shipped in January of 1979.

Value: $50-$100

Super Disk with format front closed

Super Disk opened

Electrolabs Super Disk
Type: Removable hard-disk drive.
Capacity: 10 Mby.
Physical: 12¾"W by 22½"D by 6"H, weighed 39 pounds.
Production: Available by April of 1979.
Cost: $6750.00, with controller.
This drive ran at 3600 rpm. It could be used with PDP-11, LSI-11 and S-100 machines.

Value: $40-$75

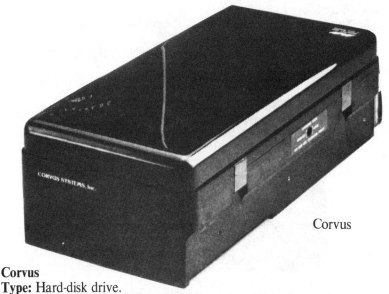

Corvus

Corvus
Type: Hard-disk drive.
Capacity: 10 Mby.
Physical: This drive, along with an "intelligent" controller, was contained in "a package smaller than a briefcase."
Production: In production by August of 1979.
Cost: $5350 for the whole system. Add-on disks were $2990 each
This drive operated on S-100 machines, TRS-80s or Apples. It had a Z-80 disk controller, and came with disk diagnostics. Each system could drive up to four disks.

Value: $50-$100

SA-4008
Shugart Associates SA-4008
Type: Hard-disk drive

(cont.)

SA 4008 (cont.)
Capacity: 29 Mby.
Speed: This drive spun "at eight times the rate of floppies."
Production: Introduced about August 1979.
Advertisements aimed this disk at "small business and professional computer users."

Value: $100-$200

M2201

Fujitsu M2201
Type: Cartridge module hard-disk drive.
Capacity: 50 Mby unformatted, or 40 Mby formatted.
Production: Introduced through MicroAge for the Alpha Micro and Horizon systems in about August of 1979.
Cost: $9995.00 for the drive, disk pack, software interface and S-100 controller.

Value: $50-$100

Phoenix

CDC Phoenix
Type: Cartridge module hard-disk drive.
Capacity: 32 Mby unformatted, or 27 Mby formatted.
Production: Introduced through MicroAge for the Alpha Micro and Horizon systems in about August of 1979.
Cost: $9995.00 for the drive, disk pack, software interface and S-100 controller.

Value: $50-$100

Konan SMC-100
Type: Hard-disk drive system.
Speed: Transferred data at 6 to 10 MHz.
Production: In production by October of 1979.
Cost: $1650.
Each system could "control up to 4 drives ranging from 8 to 600 megabytes per drive."

Value: $25-$50

Lobo
Type: Hard-disk drive.
Capacity: 10 to 40 Mby.
Production: In production by November of 1979.

This drive was advertised for the TRS-80.

Value: $25-$75

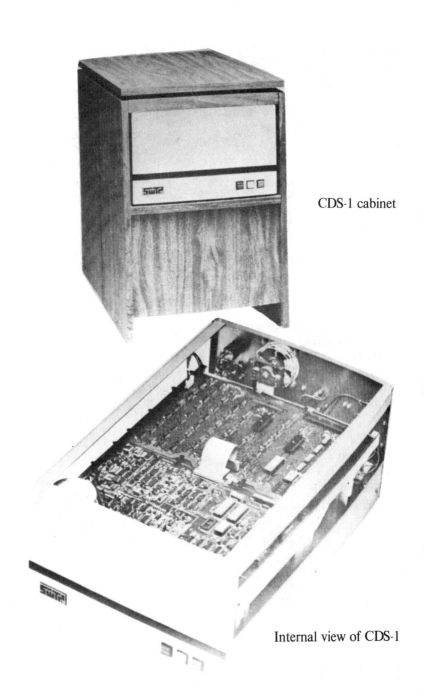

CDS-1 cabinet

Internal view of CDS-1

SWTPC (Southwest Technical Products Corp.) CDS-1
Type: Hard-disk drive.
Capacity: About 16 Mby.
Production: In production by March of 1980.
Cost: $3995.00 for drive and controller. Cabinet matching the SWTPC 6809 computer desk was $150.
The CDS-1 was compatible with the SWTPC 6809 floppy-disk system running the FLEX9 operating system.

Value: $40-$75

Seagate ST-506
Type: 5.25-inch hard-disk drive.
Capacity: 5 Mby.
Physical: A full-height IBM PC-compatible drive.
Production: Introduced about 1980.
The interface for this drive, along with the ST-406, set the ST-506/412 standard.

Value: $25-$75

Discus M26
Thinker Toys Discus M26
Type: Hard-disk drive.
Capacity: 26 Mby.
Interface: S-100 interface could drive up to four drives.
Production: In production by March of 1980.
Cost: $4995 for disk with operating system (CP/M 2.0), controller and cables. Drives alone were $4495.
Advertisements claimed the M26 was "the first 26 megabyte hard disk memory for S-100 systems." This system was based on the Shugart SA-4008 drive.

Value: $25-$75

Micropolis
Production: In production by November of 1980.

Value: $25-$75

Seagate ST-412
Type: Hard-disk drive.
Capacity: 10 Mby.
Physical: A full-height IBM PC-compatible drive.
Production: Introduced about 1981.
The interface for this drive, along with the ST-512, set the ST-506/412 standard. This drive was used in the original IBM XT.

Value: $25-$75

Apple ProFile
Capacity: 5 Mby.
Production: Introduced in September of 1981.
Cost: $3499.

Value: $40-$100

Corona Starfire
Type: Hard-disk drive.
Capacity: 5 Mby.
Production: In production by 1984.
This drive was aimed at the Apple II.

Value: $25-$50

Iomega Bernoulli Box, Alpha-10
Type: Dual 8-inch removable drive.
Capacity: 10 Mby per drive.
Physical: Removable drives were contained in a rigid cartridge.
Production: Introduced about September of 1982.
This was an early removable hard drive.

Value: $25-$75

Iomega Bernoulli Box, Beta-5
Type: 5.25-inch removable drive.
Capacity: 5 Mby.
Physical: Removable drives were contained in a rigid cartridge.
Production: Introduced about July of 1982.
This was an early removable hard drive.

Value: $25-$75

Mountain Computer
Type: Hard-disk drive.
Capacity: 5 M, 10 M, 15 M and 20 M.
Production: In production by 1984.
Cost: $1995 for 5 M, $2495 for 10 M, $2995 for 15 M, and $3495 for 20 M.
These drives were sold for the Apple II and Apple III computers.
Value: $25-$50

General Computer Hyperdrive
Type: Hard-disk drive.
Production: Introduced in 1985.
The Hyperdrive was an internal hard-disk drive for the Mac. It sold only for a while.

Value: $25-$50

251

III-3. PRINTERS:

Aside from being able to conveniently access their machines (through Teletypes or keyboards and CRTs) and storing data off-line (on cassettes or floppy disks), being able to print output was a top priority of the early personal computer users. Some of the early machines using Teletypes as a user interface incorporated a printing capability in their printed output, but these combersome interfaces were not the norm.

The first printers aimed at the personal computer market were an odd conglomeration of devices from other industries. Early technologies included mechanical devices that pushed down the keys of standard electric typewriters, electric typewriters adapted to take digital input, thermal printers, and dot-matrix printers.

As the market expanded, and the demand for speed and printing quality increased, printing technology rapidly advanced. Today, improved versions of dot-matrix printers still hold a significant portion of the market. However, ink-jet printers can rapidly produce high quality output, and the laser printers, which produce fast high-resolution output rivaling commercial printing quality, are now only slightly more expensive than ink-jets.

III-3-1. ADAPTED-TYPEWRITER PRINTERS:

One of the first hard-copy output mechanisms designed specifically for the personal computer was the adapted electric typewriter. These machines were slow and cumbersome, but gave excellent quality output. They came in basically two forms. Some typewriters were adapted to allow them to directly receive digital input from the serial or parallel I/O port of the computer, and type it out. These were sold both as kits and as converted units. The other adaptation consisted of a mechanical interface comprised of plungers positioned over each key. When the plungers were activated by signals from the computer's I/O port, they depressed the keys to "type" out the output. Both versions of typewriter conversion were quickly displaced by thermal, dot-matrix, and daisywheel printers whose versatility and speed were far superior.

H2 Digital Adapt-A-Typer
Type: Mechanical interface to electric typewriter.
Speed: The speed was "trimmed" to the maximum speed of the
typewriter, which was typically 100 words per minute.
Interface: Parallel.
Physical: The mechanics of this machine were located in a housing
that fitten over an electric typewriter keyboard. The keys of the
typewriter were depressed mechanically.
Production: In production by April of 1976.
Cost: $249 as a kit, $399.50 assembled.   **Value: $300-$400**

Edityper Systems
Type: Typewriter Conversion.
Production: In production by July of 1977.
Cost: $395.

This was advertised as an "IBM selectic typewriter input/output conver-
sion kit," and was said to be "easy to install on any IBM Selectric I and
II, providing quality hard copy for all microprocessor devices." Edityper
was a subsidiary of Tycom Corporation.
                    Value: $75-$125 for complete converted unit.

253

MCD (Micro Computer Devices) Selectra-Term
Type: Converted IBM electric typewriter.
Production: In production by July of 1978.
Cost: $1750.

This device was based on the IBM Selectric II that "has been fully converted for direct connection to your computer." It had "full ASCII and upper and lower case alphanumerics." It could be used as a typewriter.
Value: $75-$125 for complete converted unit.

H & K Singer 7100 and 7102
Type: Converted electric typewriter.
Speed: 11 to 15 cps.
Interface: RS-232 serial or current-loop.
Production: Available by September of 1978.
Cost: $650-$1295.

(cont.)

H & K Singer (cont.)

This device was available both new and reconditioned. It could be used off-line as a standard electric typewriter, and was advertised as "a professional computer terminal for the hobbyist." The 7102 model was the same as the 7101, but included a paper-tape punch and reader.

Value: $75-$125 for the 7100, $250 to $300 for the 7102

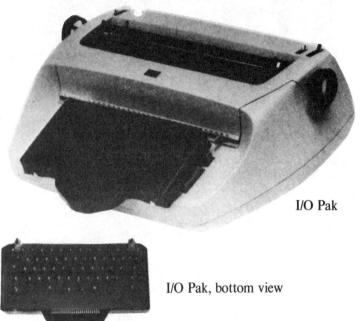

I/O Pak

I/O Pak, bottom view

Rochester Data I/O Pak
Type: Mechanical interface for electric typewriter.
Production: In production April of 1979.
Cost: $395.

This device mechanically interfaced with the keyboard of an electric typewriter. Advertisements claimed "low cost, high quality hard copy."

Value: $300-$400

Anderson Jacobson AJ 841 I/O Terminal
Type: Converted electric typewriter.
Speed: 14.7 cps.
Interface: RS-232 serial or parallel.
Production: In production by July of 1979.

The AJ 841 was a "completely refurbished 'selectric' ASCII terminal for the small business or serious hobbyist." It could also be used as a typewriter.
Value: $75-$125

Spinwriter 5530-P
(cont.)

Spinwriter (cont.)

Spinwriter with keyboard

NEC (Nippon Electric Co.) Spinwriter 5530-P
Type: Selectric-type printer.
Speed: 55 cps.
Production: Available by November of 1979.
Cost: $2995.

This device was advertised for use with the Commodore PET. It had a Centronics I/O modified for use with the PET, and typestyles could be changed by changing the thimble. IBM quality letter output was claimed.
Value: $75-$125

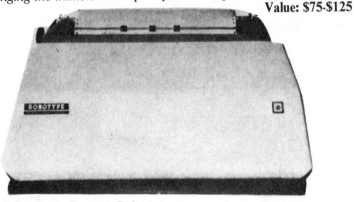

Applied Computer Systems Robotype
Type: Mechanical interface to typewriter.
Interface: Both serial and parallel interfaces. Compatible with the Centronics interface.
Production: Introduced about December of 1979.
Cost: Under $1000.
Advertisements claimed the Robotype "Connects to IBM Selectric II typewriter in just one minute," and "Adapts to a variety of typewriters - no modifications." It was advertised for use with TRS-80, Apple II, PET and others. **Value: $300-$400**

257

III-3-2. THERMAL AND ELECTROSENSITIVE PRINTERS:

The thermal and electrosensitive printers were early forms of inexpensive yet versatile hard-copy output. As with dot-matrix printers, these devices were able to print a wide range of print styles (since each character was comprised of a series of dots). Resolutions were poor and they required special paper that could respond to the thermal or electrical output from the printhead.

The electrosensitive printers created output by electrically removing a cover layer or coating on the paper to expose dark material beneath. The thermal printers used heat to activate sensitive paper. Drawbacks of these technologies included expensive paper, often in nonstandard widths, and, in the case of the thermal printers, fading with time. Both technologies were collectively referred to as "non-impact."

These devices were ultimately displaced by the dot-matrix and daisywheel printers, which could print on conventional paper of standard dimensions. The technology is still found in some very small portable printers, but these devices are seldom sold for microcomputer output applications.

Bowmar TP-3120
Type: Thermal.
Speed: 29.4 cps, 1.07 lines per second.
Interface: 12-position dual-readout connector.
Production: Introduced about August of 1976.
Cost: $149.

This device printed 5-by-5 matrix characters in an 18-column format. It had alpha-numeric capabilities.   **Value: $50-$75**

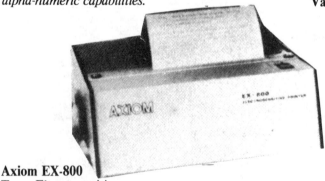

EX-800

Axiom EX-800
Type: Electrosensitive.
Speed: 160 cps.
Interface: Serial interface, RS-232C or current-loop.
Physical: 9.625" by 3.875" by 10.825", weighed 12 pounds.
Production: Introduced at the NCC show in June 1977.
Cost: $655.
(cont.)

258

Axiom (cont.)

The EX-800 printed 20, 40 or 80 characters per inch from a 96-character ASCII generator, on 5-inch wide electrosensitive paper that cost about $3 per roll. It used an Intel 4004 processor for control, had a self-test feature, and a 128-character buffer.

Value: $50-$75

Telpar

Telpar PS-40
Type: Thermal.
Speed: 20 cps.
Interface: TTL level parallel interface with handshaking.
Production: In production by July of 1977.
Cost: $250 for mechanism and print head, $350 with TTL parallel interface as a kit, $400 assembled, $550 with RS-232C interface (assembled).

The PS-40 printed 64 upper case ASCII characters in 48-column-wide lines.
Value: $40-$75

Syntest SP-302 Digital Printer
Type: Thermal.
Speed: 50-cps printing rate, 110-bps data rate.
Interface: RS-232 or 20 mA current-loop.
Production: Introduced about May of 1978.
Cost: $575.

The SP-302 was a microprocessor-controlled printer. It could print 40 characters per line and had double and triple spacing, and double-width printing.
Value: $40-$75

Perkin-Elmer Terminals Division Pussycat 650 CRT Printer
Type: Thermal.
Speed: 100 cps.
Physical: 4" by 12" by 12", weighed 15 pounds.
Production: In production by April of 1978.
Cost: $795 in OEM lots of 75.

Advertisements claimed this printer was "capable of printing full 1920 character cathode ray tube screens in less than 20 seconds." It printed in a 24-line by 80-character format using a 9-by-12 format 96-character ASCII set on standard paper. A Motorola 6800 microprocessor controlled the dot heating.

Value: $40-$75

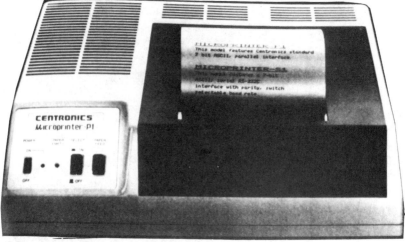

Microprinter P1

Centronics P1 and S1
Type: Non-impact.
Speed: 150 lines per minute.
Interface: The P-1 had a parallel interface, and the S-1 had a serial interface.
Production: In production by March of 1978.
Cost: Priced near $600 initially, was offered at $395 by August of 1978.

This printer printed 80-column lines.

Value: $50-$100

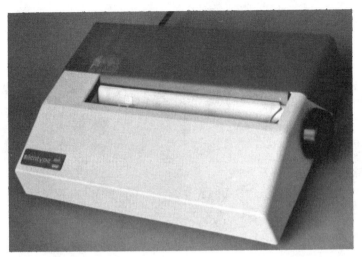

Silentype

Silentype manual

Apple Silentype
Production: Introduced in June of 1979.
This was the first printer offered by Apple.   **Value: $50-$125**

EX-801

Axiom EX-801 MicroPrinter
Type: Electrosensitive.
Speed: Up to 160 cps.
Interface: Had both serial and parallel interfaces.
Physical: Advertising copy for this machine and the EX-820 read, "These babies are beautiful, housed in sleek molded cases designed by the award-winning Inova design group."
Production: In production by June of 1978.
Cost: $655.

This printer was based on the Intel 8048 processor. It had three character sizes that gave 80-, 40-, or 20-column line-widths, and printed on 5-inch wide paper. Its standard 256-character buffer was expandable to 2 K. Its 96-character capability could also be expanded.

Value: $50-$75

PS-48E

Telpar PS-48E
Type: Thermal.
Speed: 24 cps. 110 to 300 Baud in serial, up to 960 cps parallel.
Interface: RS-232C, 20 mA loop, or TTL parallel.
Production: Available by November of 1978.
Cost: $450.

This machine was microprocessor controlled. It had 96 upper and lower case ASCII characters.

Value: $40-$75

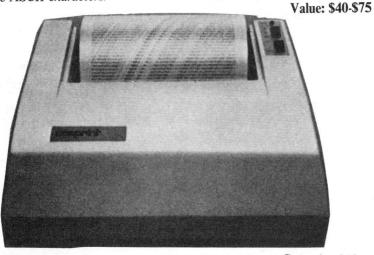

Comprint 912

Comprint 912
Type: Non-impact.
Speed: 225 cps.
Interface: Both parallel and serial were available.
Production: In production by May of 1979.

(cont.)

263

Comprint 912 (cont.)
Cost: $560

This machine printed 80-character lines of 9-by-12 characters on 8.5-inch wide "silver paper" (aluminum coated paper).

Value: $40-$75

PET 2021

Commodore PET 2021 Series Printer
Type: Electrostatic.
Production: Introduced about summer of 1979.
Cost: $550.

Value: $50-$75

Trendcom 100 Intelligent Printer
Type: Thermal.
Speed: 40 cps.
Interface: Interfaces were available for PET, Sorcerer, TRS-80 and Apple II.
Physical: Advertisements claimed it was "Fully enclosed in a metal and high-impact plastic case and is available in both 115 V and 230 V AC versions."
Production: In production by December of 1979.
Cost: $375.

This device printed 40-column wide output on 4.5-inch wide paper. It could print the 96-character ASCII set bidirectionally in a 5-by-7 format.

Value: $40-$75

III-3-3. DAISYWHEEL PRINTERS:

The technology of the daisywheel printers is close to that of the adapted-typewriter printers. In fact some daisywheel printers had keyboards and could be used as typewriters. A daisywheel printer's printable characters were molded in type at the ends of small, flexible arms radiating out from a center hub. A hammer struck the end of the arm which then printed the character using an inked ribbon, in the manner of a typewriter. Rotating the hub changed characters.

Daisywheel printers typically printed at 10 - 60 cps, and thus were similar in speed to the Teletypes. In the mid to late 1970s, daisywheels were used for high-quality output, while dot-matrix printers were used for speed. With the increase in quality of the dot-matrix printers in the early 1980s, the market for daisywheels died off.

Qume Sprint Micro 5
Type: Daisywheel.
Speed: Available in 45-and-55-cps models.
Interface: A parallel interface was standard, an RS-232C serial interface was optional.
Production: Introduced about February of 1978.
Cost: 45-cps model was $1675.

This was an OEM product that may have been sold under the name "Sprint Micro 5." It had a built-in microprocessor and a set of 58 commands that could set character spacing, hammer intensity, ribbon color, and normal or graphics mode.

Value: $50-$100

Diablo 1200

Xerox Diablo 1200
Type: Daisywheel.
This unit was also referred to as the Diablo HyType I.   **Value: $50-$75**

Algorithmics PR-DW1
Type: Daisywheel
Speed: 45 cps (bidirectionally). A 55-cps version was also available.
Interface: Parallel.
Production: Introduced about September of 1978.
Cost: $2678.

The PR-DW1 had a host microprocessor.

Value: $40-$75

Diablo 1620

Xerox Diablo 1620
Type: Daisywheel.
Production: In production by July of 1979.
Cost: $3240 list.

This unit was also referred to in some Advertisements as the Diablo HyTerm II.

Value: $50-$75

Diablo 1640

Xerox Diablo 1640
Type: Daisywheel

(cont.)

266

Xerox (cont.)
Speed: 45 cps.
Production: Introduced about May of 1979.
Cost: $2690, or $2331 for receive-only.

Value: $50-$75

Diablo 1650 manual

Xerox Diablo 1650
Type: Metal daisywheel.
Speed: 40 cps.
Production: Introduced about May of 1979.
Cost: $2779, or $2419 for receive-only.

Value: $50-$75

Diablo 1660

Xerox Diablo 1660
Type: Daisywheel
Production: In production by October of 1977.   **Value: $50-$75**

IPSI
Type: Daisywheel.
Speed: 45 cps.
Interface: RS-232C at 110, 150, 300, and 1200 Baud.
Production: In production by July of 1979.
Cost: $2595.

Advertisements for the IPSI claimed "Over 30 print wheels from 10 to 15 char/inch". "Identical in every respect to it's high priced sister the Diablo HyTerm II model 1620."

Value: $25-$75

AC-14

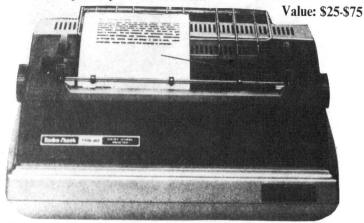

OSI (Ohio Scientific Instruments) AC-14
Type: Daisywheel.
Speed: 55 cps.
Interface: Parallel.
Production: In production by October of 1977.
Cost: $2795.

The AC-14 could print up to 132 columns.

Value: $25-$75

Tandy/Radio-Shack TRS-80 Daisy Wheel Printer
Type: Daisywheel.
Production: In production by March of 1980.

(cont.)

TRS-80 (cont.)
Cost: $2999.

This printer was advertised as part of a word-processing system incorporating the Scripsit word processor and a new upper and lower-case kit for the TRS-80 computer.

Value: $25-$75

Diablo 630

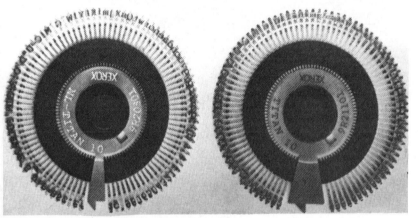

Diablo 630 print wheels

Xerox Diablo 630
Type: Daisywheel
Production: In production by May of 1980.

The 630 could use four different types of print wheels, including both plastic and metal.

Value: $20-$50

III-3-4. DOT-MATRIX PRINTERS:

The term "dot-matrix" typically refers to any of the pin-impact printers using a matrix of pins to impact an inked ribbon and create a dot image of character on the underlying paper. The nomenclature is somewhat confusing, however since thermal and electrosensitive printers also created dot-matrix characters. The term "impact" was also used to refer to daisywheel printers as well as pin-impact printers. Here, however, the term "dot-matrix" is used to refer only to pin-impact printers.

Dot-matrix printers initially employed 9 impact pins to make up the character matrix, but in the early 1980s 24-pin heads were introduced. Unlike daisywheel printers, which could only print the characters molded on their printwheels, dot-matrix printers were typically microprocessor-controller and could print a range of character styles. As time passed, graphics capability became a standard feature of dot-matrix printers. The principle advantage of the dot-matrix over the daisywheel was printing speed and versatility. The main disadvantage was print quality, but as dot-matrix machines improved, this difference became less pronounced.

7040

MITS (Micro Instrumentation and Telemetry Systems) Altair 110
Type: Dot matrix.
Speed: 100 cps, 70 lines per second.
Production: In production by December of 1975.
Cost: $1750 as a kit, $1975 assembled.

This printer printed 80 columns of 5-by-7 dot matrix characters. It printed bidirectionally on an 8.5-inch roll of paper.

Value: $200-$300

270

7040

7040-T

C.Itoh Electronics 7040 and 7040-T
Type: Dot matrix.
Production: In production by July of 1976.

This printer had 3.5-inch print line capacity, and printed on a 3 7/8-inch roll or ticket. It could print 40 columns at 12 characters per inch, with variable font and density capability under software control. Both models 7040 and 7040-T were available.

Value: $50-$75

SWTPC (Southwest Technical Products Corp.) PR-40 Alphanumeric Printer
Type: Dot matrix.
Speed: 75 lines per minute.
Interface: Parallel.
Physical: 9.625" by 10.50" by 8.75".
Production: In production by August of 1976.

(cont.)

Cost: $250 as a kit.

This printer printed 5-by-7 dot characters on 3.875-inch adding machine paper. It could print the 64-character upper case ASCII set at 40 characters per line, and was advertised for use with the SWTPC 6800 and MITS Altair 8800. The mechanism was claimed to be an OEM printer used in "point of sale" terminals and electronic cash registers. It had a 40-character buffer.

Value: $50-$100

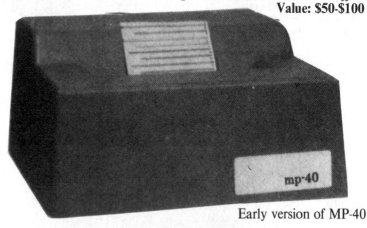

Early version of MP-40

Later version of MP-40

MPI (Micro Peripherals, Inc.) MP-40
Type: Dot matrix.
Speed: 75 lines per minute.
Physical: It's molded plastic case was 13" by 13" by 6.5".
Production: Introduced about August of 1976.
Cost: The SSP-40 was $575, the MP-40 was $425, and the KP-40 kit was $179.

This device printed 40 columns of 5-by-7 characters on 4-inch wide adding-

272 (cont.)

MPI-40 (cont.)

machine paper. The SSP-40 had its own microprocessor for connection to the serial port, the MP-40 interfaced through the parallel port, and the KP-40 kit contained the mechanism and minimum electronics for connection to the parallel port.

Value: $40-$75

Tally T132
Type: Dot matrix printer.
Interface: Parallel.
Production: In production by March of 1977.
Cost: $950.

This device printed in a 132-column width, and could print forms up to 14 7/8" wide. It had a single line of dynamic memory. It may have been a surplus machine sold into the personal computer market.

Value: $25-$75

Digital Group Printer

Digital Group Printer, internal view

The Digital Group
Type: Impact printer.
Speed: 120 cps.
Interface: 8-bit parallel.
Production: In production by March of 1977.
Cost: Available as a kit for $495.

This full-size impact printer printed 5-by-7 dot characters at 96 characters per line, (12 characters per inch horizontal), and 6 lines per inch vertical. It could print up to four copies simultaneously, and had a built-in ribbon re-inker. A 10,000,000 character life was claimed. It used either an 8½-inch roll or fanfold paper.   **Value: $40-$75**

Peripheral Vision

Peripheral Vision
Type: Impact printer.
Speed: 120 cps.
Interface: 8-bit parallel.
Production: In production by April of 1977.
Cost: $495 as a kit.   (cont.)

274

Peripheral Vision (cont.)

This machine printed 5-by-7 characters at 96 characters per line (12 characters per inch horizontal), and 6 lines-per-inch. It used a re-inkable ribbon, and printed on 8.5-inch roll or fan-fold paper.

Value: $40-$75

MPI (Micro Peripherals, Inc.) SSP-40
Type: Dot matrix.
Speed: 75 lines per minute.
Production: In production by July of 1977.
Cost: $575.

Advertising copy for the SSP-40 stated it "contains its own microprocessor for easy connection to your serial port." It printed 5-by-7 impact dot-matrix characters at up to 40 columns per line.

Value: $40-$75

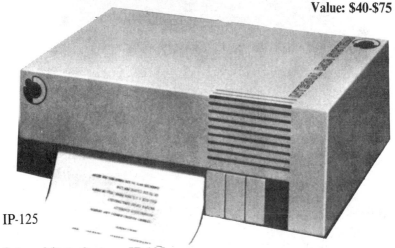

IP-125

Integral Data Systems IP-125
Type: Dot matrix.
Speed: Could print at 50 cps, with an instantaneous rate of 100 cps.
Interface: RS-232 or current-loop.
Production: Introduced late in 1977.
Cost: $745

This device printed the standard ASCII set of 64 characters in a 5-by-7 format in up to 132 characters per line. The ribbon was automatically re-inked during printing. Advertisements claimed it was "A complete professional printer that's fully assembled, tested and ready to use," "no special software to write...and no need, either, for expensive special paper."

Value: $25-$75

Integral Data Systems IP-225
Type: Dot matrix.
Speed: Could print at instantaneous rates of 165 cps, and a sustained print rate of 80 cps.
Production: In production by February of 1978.
Cost: $949 assembled.

This enhanced version of the IP-125 had 132 character line lengths, variable print densities, and a full CRT screen size buffer that could hold 2048 characters. It could print graphics symbols and had selectable form sizes, and automatic line-feed on carriage return.

Value: $25-$75

779

Centronics 703 and 779 printers
Type: Dot matrix.
Production: In production by January of 1978.

The 770 printer was $1099, the 703 serial printer was $2395, and the 761 printer with keyboard was $1695.

Value: $40-$75

Anadex DP-1000
Type: Dot matrix.
Speed: 110 to 2400 bps. Could print 1.25 40-character lines per second.
Interface: RS-232C.
Production: Introduced about March of 1978.
Cost: Less than $700.

This printer could print 64 alphanumeric and special characters. It used standard single or multiple copy paper rolls.

Value: $25-$75

Motorola Semiconductor Products EXORprint Printer
Type: Impact printer.
Speed: 110 cps.
Production: Introduced about March of 1978.
Cost: $1725.

This device printed 5-by-7 characters bidirectionally at up to 80 characters per line. It used 8.5-inch wide roll paper and a conventional Teletype ribbon.
Value: $40-$75

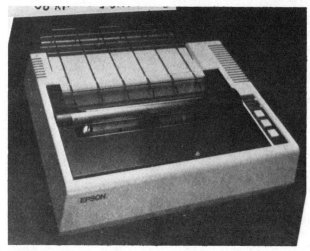

MX-80

Epson MX-80
Type: Dot matrix.
Production: Introduced in 1978.

The MX-80 expanded the market for low-cost printers. It was very popular.
Value: $100-$200

Motorola Microsystems 700 Series printers (702, 703, 779, 781)
Type: Dot matrix.
Speed: 702: 120 cps, 703: 180 cps, 779: 60 cps, 781: 120 lines per minute.
Production: Introduced about August of 1978.
Cost: 702: $2500, 703: $3125, 779: $1495, 781: $2095.

The 702 printed 132-column lines, the 779 printed from 80 to 132 columns of 5-by-7 characters, the 781 printed 80-column lines.
Value: $25-$75

ibs (independent business systems) Centronics 779
Type: Dot matrix.
Speed: 60 cps.
Production: Available by April of 1979.
Cost: $1095.

This machine was the Centronics model 779 with a tractor feed, a paper stacker and an ibs label on it.

Value: $50-$75

Commodore PET 2023 Series Printer
Type: Dot matrix.
Speed: 112 cps.
Production: In production by April of 1979.
Cost: $849.

This machine was controlled by a 6504 microprocessor, and had 500 bytes of RAM. It printed 7-by-6 dot matrix characters.

Value: $50-$100

Printer Terminals 879
Type: Dot matrix.
Speed: 120 cps.
Interface: RS-232 or parallel.
Production: Introduced about June of 1979.
Cost: $1395.

This device printed the full 96-character ASCII set. It could print in 80 or 132 column formats (selectable by a switch), and either 9-by-7 or 9-by-9 characters. It had 2 K or memory, and could print on paper rolls or with a tractor feed.

Value: $25-$75

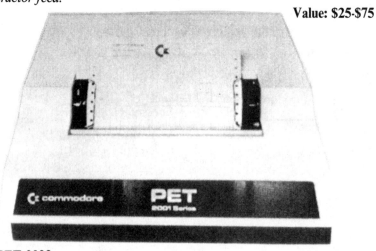

PET 2022   (cont.)

PET 2022 (cont.)
Commodore PET 2022 Series Printer
Type: Dot matrix.
Speed: 112 cps.
Production: Introduced about summer of 1979.
Cost: $995.

This tractor-feed printer could print all the PET characters (upper and lower case letters, numbers and graphics). It had bidirectional printing, was controlled by a 6504 microprocessor, and had 500 bytes of RAM. It printed 7-by-6 dot-matrix characters.

Value: $40-$75

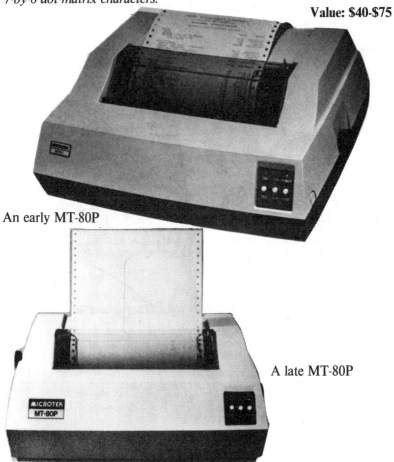

An early MT-80P

A late MT-80P

Microtek MT-80P
Type: Dot matrix.
Speed: 120 cps.
Interface: Parallel was standard, but serial RS-232 and IEEE-488 were also available.

(cont.)

MT-80P (cont.)

Production: In production by August of 1979.
Cost: $750.

This device could print on pin-feed or plain paper, in 80 or 120-column format. Paper widths ranged from 4.5 to 9.5 inches. It printed 96 ASCII characters in a 9-by-7, or 7-by-7 matrix.

Value: $25-$75

Centronics 779
Type: Dot matrix.
Speed: 60 cps.
Production: Available by September of 1979.

This machine was also sold under the ibs label.

Value: $40-$75

730

Centronics 730
Type: Dot matrix.
Speed: 50 cps.
Physical: Was about the size of a portable typewriter. Weighed less than 10 pounds.
Production: In production by September of 1979.
Cost: $75 to $125.

This printer printed 7-by-7 dot matrix characters.

Value: $50-$10

700

Centronics 700
Type: Impact printer.
Speed: 60 cps.
Production: Available by September of 1979.

Advertisements for the 700 claimed it could print forms.

Value: $40-$75

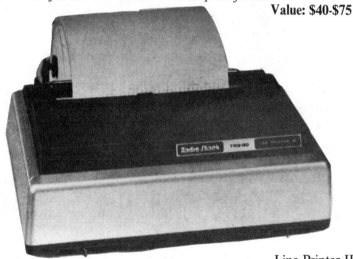

Line Printer II

Tandy/Radio Shack TRS-80 Line Printer II
Type: Dot matrix.
Speed: 50 cps.
Production: Available by September of 1979.
Cost: $999, including interface cable 26-1416 (available alone for $59).

The model number of this device was 26-1154. It printed 80 7-by-7 characters on 8-inch wide lines on 9.5-inch wide paper, but could print wider (expanded) characters. Advertisement claimed it could operate with a Level II TRS-80 computer system, and that it "Doesn't require special paper - you can use inexpensive rolls (available at Radio Shack), continuous forms (original and up to two carbons) or single sheets."

Value: $40-$75

281

701

Centronics 701
Type: Impact printer.
Speed: 60 cps.
Production: In production by September of 1979.
This device printed bidirectionally in a 132-column format.

Value: $40-$75

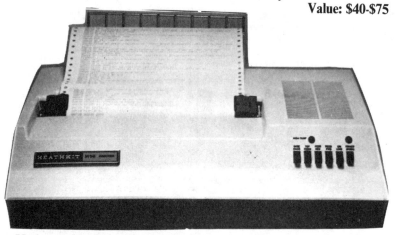

H14

Heath Data Systems H14 and WH14
Type: Dot matrix.
Interface: RS-232 or 20 mA current-loop.
Production: In production by October of 1979.
Cost: $895.

This device printed 5-by-7 characters, in upper and lower case, with variable width. It was microprocessor-controlled.

Value: $40-$75

88T

MPI (Micro Peripherals, Inc.) 88T
Type: Dot matrix.
Speed: 100 cps.
Interface: Both serial and parallel interfaces were available.
Production: In production by November of 1979.
Cost: $749.

This device could handle paper widths from 1 to 9.5 inches, and print in 80, 96 and 132-column formats. Printing was bidirectional. It had both tractor feed and pressure feeds, and could use 8.5-inch wide roll paper. It had microprocessor-control.

Value: $25-$75

AC-9TP

OSI (Ohio Scientific Instruments) AC-9TP
Type: Impact.
Speed: 110 cps.
Interface: Parallel.
Cost: $1250.

The AC-9TP could print in 80 or 132 column widths. **Value: $25-$75**

283

AC-5A

OSI (Ohio Scientific Instruments) AC-5A
Type: Impact.
Speed: 160 132-character lines per minute.
Interface: Parallel.
Cost: $2950.

The AC-5A has 12 programmable fonts and could print in upper and lower case.

Value: $25-$75

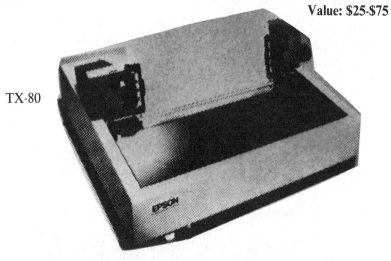

TX-80

Epson TX-80
Type: Dot matrix.
Production: In production by October of 1980.
Cost: $699.

Value: $50-$75

Epson FX-100 +
Type: Dot matrix.

This was an early wide-carriage dot-matrix printer.

Value: $50-$75

III-3-5. INK-JET PRINTERS:

Introduced in the late 1970s, ink-jet printers were initially troubled with problems handling the liquid ink. These included smearing, clogging, fading, and water solubility. As time passed, these problems were solved, and now ink-jet printers are reliable high-quality machines. The technology is often used in portable printers.

Silonics Quietype
Type: Ink jet.
Speed: 180 cps.
Interface: RS-232 serial.
Production: In production by November of 1978.
Cost: $2495 for the printer. Ink cartridges were $17.50.

The Quietype had a 96-character ASCII set and printed 80 characters per line, but could also operate in a 132-character-per-line compressed mode. Ink was delivered to the print head by a flexible tube, and printing was on rolls of class II Teletype paper.

Value: $50-$75

III-3-6. PLOTTERS:

While the early printers gave character-based output, they typically had poor graphics capability, or, more commonly, none at all. Plotters of various sorts appeared to fill this need. As time passed, graphics capability became more common in conventional printers. However, plotters are still useful for high-quality, large-size, and multi-color outputs.

Axiom EX-820 MicroPlotter
Type: Plotter.
Interface: Had both serial and parallel interfaces.
Physical: 11" by 4¼" by 12", and weighed 12 pounds with a 230 paper roll.
Production: Introduced about mid-1977.
Cost: $795.

This device had all the character-printing functions of the EX-801, but could "mix alphanumeric ASCII and graphics on any line." It had three resolutions, with the maximum being 128 dots per inch horizontal, 65 dots per inch vertical. It used the Intel 8048.

Value: $40-$75

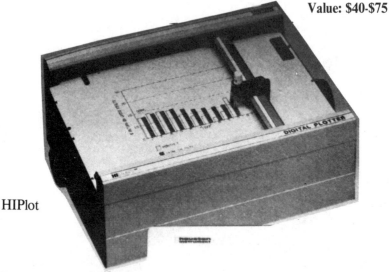

HIPlot

Houston Instrument HIPlot
Type: Plotter.
Speed: 2.4 lines per second.
Interface: Had both serial and parallel interfaces.
Production: Introduced in 1978.
Cost: $1085.

(cont.)

HIPlot (cont.)

*This plotter used standard 8.5-by-11-inch paper. It had both 0.01 and 0.005"
resolution, and variable Baud rate and step size. A liquid crystal display
showing X and Y coordinates was available as an option. It was a companion to the HIPad.*

Value: $40-$75

Sylvanhills Laboratory X-Y Plotter
Type: Plotter.
Speed: 2.5 inches per second maximum.
Interface: Parallel.
Production: In production by June of 1979.
Cost: $1049 for assembled Unit-1, $1249 for assembled Unit-2. A manual
was available for $5.

*This device plotted at 0.01 inches per pulse, with 0.005 inches per pulse
optional. Unit-1 was 11" by 17" and Unit-2 was 17" by 22".*

Value: $25-$50

III-4. DISPLAYS AND TERMINALS:

A CRT display is such a standard feature of personal computers today that it is hard to imagine a machine without it. However, the first personal computers were able to only indicate single numbers at a time through
rows of binary LEDs, or, at best, short rows of hexadecimal characters.
Teletypes offered a slow hard-copy output.

Shortly after the introduction of the first Altair, companies like Processor Technology and Polymorphic Systems were offering cards to allow
S-100 machines to drive CRTs. While the first cards typically drove television sets, the demand for increased resolution was immediate and CRTs
specifically aimed at the personal computer market appeared.

VLCT

(cont.)

VLCT (cont.)

MITS (Micro Instrumentation and Telemetry Systems) Altair VLCT (Very Low Cost Terminal)
Type: Terminal.
Production: In production by December of 1975.
Cost: $129 as a kit, $169 assembled.

This device converted three-digit octal code to eight-digit binary code to communicate with the Altair 8800.

Value: $150-$200

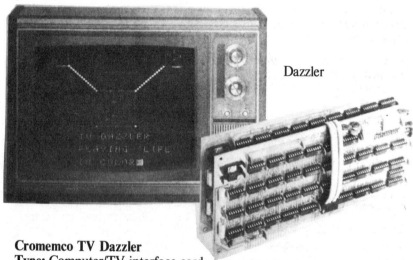

Dazzler

Cromemco TV Dazzler
Type: Computer/TV interface card.
Physical: S-100 plug-in card.
Production: Introduced prior to March of 1976.
Cost: $215 as a kit, $350 assembled.

This card was introduced for the Altair 8800 or IMSAI 8080. It could display characters or graphics in color, and had 128-by-128 picture elements. The Dazzler and Proc Tech's VDM were the first graphics cards for the Altair.

Value: $100-$200

Processor Technology Corp VDM
Type: Video board.
Production: Released in 1976.

The VDM was made for the Altair. It and Cromemco's TV Dazzler were the first graphics cards for the Altair.

Value: $50-$125

Polymorphic Systems
Type: Video terminal.
Production: In production by April of 1976.
Cost: $160 as a kit, $230 assembled, 64 character option was $25.

*This S-100 device drove a standard TV monitor, and displayed 16 lines of
64 or 32 7-by-9 dot-matrix characters from a 128 set of upper and lower
case ASCII characters and 64 graphics characters.*

Value: $50-$125

Heath Data Systems H9 Terminal
Type: Terminal.
Production: In production by April of 1978.
Cost: $530.

*This terminal had an ASCII keyboard and a 12-inch CRT. Advertisements
claimed it was "...designed for hobbyists just like you." It displayed 80
characters per line.*

Value: $50-$100

Datamedia Elite 3052A Video Terminal
Type: Terminal
Interface: EIA or 20 mA current-loop. Transmission rates as high as 9600
bps.
Production: Introduced about April 1979.
Cost: $1700.

*This was a DEC VT-52 compatible terminal. It had one page of video
memory, and included a detached keyboard. It could display 24 lines of 80
characters each.*

Value: $25-$75

AC-7B

OSI (Ohio Scientific Instruments) AC-7B
Type: CRT terminal
Production: In production by April of 1980.
Cost: $995.

(cont.)

AC-7B (cont.)
The AC-7B displayed 24 lines of 80 characters each. It could display upper and lower case, and had a numeric keypad.

Value: $25-$75

III-5. MEMORY:

When the Altair 8800 was introduced in 1975, one kilobyte of RAM was a considerable amount. However, as in all other areas of the personal computer market, more capability was soon available for less money. By 1985 one megabyte of RAM was considered reasonable in a mid-range personal computer. Today, RAM is measured in units of megabytes, and memory capacities of 32 megabytes and 64 megabytes are discussed in the same manner as 32 kilobytes and 64 kilobytes were fifteen years ago.

However, as RAM has become more cheap and plentiful, the demand for RAM by operating systems and programs has grown. The days of a user running Tiny BASIC in a few kilobytes of RAM are gone. System owners keep up with the growing demands of software on RAM through several memory-addition standards. While for a time memory was added using expansion boards on the system bus, now it is expanded through 1 and 4 megabyte SIMMs and SIPs that plug directly onto the motherboard.

S.D. Sales Co.
Production: In production by October of 1975.

This card used Intel 1 K, 650 ns, static RAM. These cost 3.95 each or 8 for $30.

Value: $20-$50

CMR Computer Mfg. Co.
Speed: 350 ns access time.
Capacity: 8192 words of dynamic RAM.
Physical: S-100 card.
Production: In production by October of 1975.
Cost: $599.

This card had 8K-by-8 dynamic RAM, and was designed for the Altair.

Value: $20-$50

Processor Technology Corp memory card
Type: Memory card.
Physical: S-100 card.

Processor Technology was started to supply memory boards for Altair computers, but later built its own personal computers.

Value: $50-$100

Centi-Byte
Production: In production by October of 1975.

This card used Signetics 2602-1 1-K 475 ns static RAM. They cost $4.25 for one, $4.00 each for eight, or $3.75 each for 32.

Value: $20-$50

Dutronics
Type: Memory card.
Speed: 420 ns.
Capacity: 16,384 8-bit words on one card.
Production: In production by December of 1975.
Cost: $895.

Value: $20-$50

IMSAI (IMS Associates, Inc.)
Type: Memory card.
Speed: 450 ns.
Capacity: 4 K.
Physical: S-100 card.
Production: In production by June of 1976.
Cost: $139

Billed as compatible with the Altair 8800, this card had LEDs that showed status information of the memory blocks.

Value: $40-$75

16KZ

16KZ manual

Cromemco 16 KZ
Type: Memory card.
Capacity: 16 K.
Physical: S-100 card.
Production: Introduced about 1977.

Value: $50-$75

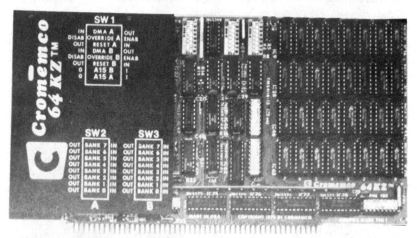

Cromemco 64KZ
Type: Memory card.
Speed: 150 ns access time.
Capacity: 64 K.
Physical: S-100 card.
Production: In production by July of 1979.
Cost: $1785.

(cont.)

64KZ (cont.)

This card was claimed to operate in "fast Z-80 systems with no wait states." It had the legend for the three dip switches marked on the heat-sink. Advertising copy read "Here's 64 kilobytes of memory on one RAM card. Yes, we mean 512K bits of read/write memory on this single card."

Value: $40-$75

Godbout Econoram II
Type: Memory card.
Physical: S-100 card.
Production: Introduced about 1977.

Value: $40-$75

Omni Systems
Type: Memory card.
Speed: 200 ns.
Capacity: 16 K static RAM.
Physical: S-100 card.
Production: In production by March of 1977.
Cost: $495 as a kit, $529 assembled. A paging option was available for $9.

This card was advertised for the Altair, IMSAI and Poly 88.

Value: $20-$50

Prime Radix Computer Synthesis
Type: memory card.
Speed: 300 ns worst-case access time.
Capacity: 40 K for $1490, 48 K for $1580, 56 K for $1670, 64 K for $1750.
Production: In production by March of 1977.

This card had fully buffered RAM, and presented one TTL load to the bus.

Value: $20-$50

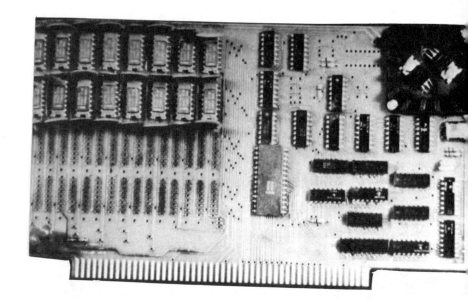

Central Data 16 K RAM Board
Speed: 450 ns.
Physical: S-100 card.
Production: In production by January of 1978.
Cost: This card came assembled for $299. The 32 K card was $525.

This 16 K card could be expanded to 32 K.

Value: $20-$50

MSI (Midwest Scientific Instruments) RAM-68
Production: In production by April of 1977.
Cost: $249.

This was an 8 K RAM card for the SWTP 6800.

Value: $30-$75

Dynabyte
Type: Memory card.
Capacity: 16,384 bytes.
Physical: S-100 card.
Production: In production by April of 1977.
Cost: $485.

This card came with a one-year guarantee.

Value: $20-$50

Solid State Sales Universal 4 K Memory Board Kit
Type: Memory card.
Production: In production by December of 1977.
Cost: $74.50.

This card could be used by the KIM-1. It used 32-2102 static RAM and had 16 address lines.

Value: $20-$50

III-6. COMMUNICATIONS:

One of the most appealing features of personal computers is their ability to operate autonomously, without the requirement of being tied to a mainframe or minicomputer for their data and processing capabilities. However, the usefulness of a personal computer can be greatly enhanced by linking it to the other personal computers or to information services. This can be done through direct links or through modems.

Communication to and from microcomputers dates back to their introduction, and today has grown into a major industry. The national communications networks and the thousands of bulletin-board systems worldwide all reflect the growing trend of communications between microcomputers. While acoustic modems were initially used to connect dumb terminals to remote host mainframe or minicomputer systems, on the arrival of the microcomputer, they were used to interconnect remote personal computers. Modem connections between microcomputers and various remote machines came to form a critical link in the world-wide networks used today.

Besides telephone-line connections, direct connections through the various I/O ports of the early microcomputers were used from the beginning to transfer information between machines. This type of connection evolved into the interconnection systems that are today's local area networks, or LANs.

Tri-Tec
Type: Acoustic-coupler modem.
Production: In production by January of 1976.

Value: $20-$50

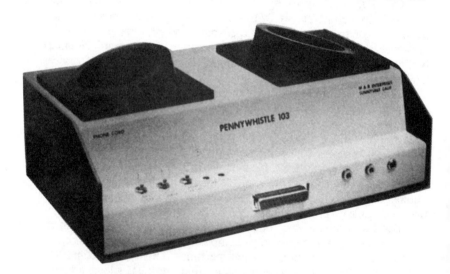

M & R Enterprises Pennywhistle 103 Modem
Type: Acoustic-coupler modem.
Production: In production by November of 1976.
Cost: $109.95.

Sold as a kit, this modem could operate in half-duplex or full-duplex modes.
Value: $15-$40

Executive Devices PDT-700 (Pocket Data Terminal)
Type: Touch terminal frequency generator, to be used with a portable data terminal.
Physical: This unit was battery-powered.
Production: In production by November of 1976.
Cost: $39.95 as a kit, $49.95 assembled.

Advertising copy for the PDT-700 read "Generates the full 16 combinations of tones possible with the touch tone encoding technique, and interfaces with the telephone network through an acoustic coupler."
Value: $15-$40

Executive Devices PDT-1000 (Pocket Data Terminal)
Production: In production by November of 1976.
Cost: $69.95 as a kit, $89.95 assembled.

This device was similar to PDT-700, but had a nonvolatile memory for automatic dialing.
Value: $15-$40

Anderson Jacobson A 242A
Type: Acoustic-coupler modem.
Speed: Operated at a rate of up to 450 bps in the send mode.
Interface: RS-232 and 20 mA.
Physical: Had flush-mounted acoustic cups.
Production: In production by October of 1977.
Cost: $365.

Value: $20-$50

ElCom

ElCom 30 and 32
Type: Acoustic-coupler modem.
Speed: 300 bps.
Interface: RS-232 or 20 mA current-loop interfaces.
Production: In production by December of 1977.

The model 30 was originate-only, and the model 32 was originate and answer. Both were Bell 103/113 compatible.
Value: $15-$40

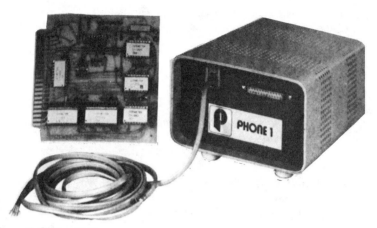

Phone 1 Cheap Talk
Speed: Ran at Baud rates from 0 to 300.
Physical: Dimensions of the cabinet were: 7¼" long, 5½" wide, and 3⅛" high.
Production: In production by March of 1978.
Cost: Available as PC board only for $115, or complete and packaged with DB-25S connector and 6-foot long telephone line for $133.

Cheap Talk was a full duplex, 103-type modem.   **Value: $15-$40**

datec 30 and 32
Type: Acoustic-coupler modem.
Speed: 300 bps.
Physical: Self-contained unit.
Production: In production by June of 1978.

This early modem was Bell 103/113 compatible, and could operate in duplex or half-duplex modes. The 30 was an originate-only unit, and the 32 was originate and answer unit.

Value: $15-$40

298

USR-310

USR-330

U.S. Robotics USR-310, 320, and 330
Type: Acoustic-coupler modem.
Speed: 300 Baud.
Interface: Available with serial or parallel interface.
Physical: Self-contained unit.
Production: In production by June of 1978.
Cost: $139 for 310, $160 for 320, $185 for 330. Higher prices for direct-connect types.

This modem came fully assembled, and could operate in full or half-duplex mode. The 310 was an originate-only unit, the 320 was an auto-answer unit, and the 330 was an originate and auto-answer unit.

Value: $20-$40

80-103A

D.C. Hayes Associates 80-103A Data Communications Adapter
Type: Internal modem.
Physical: A single S-100 card.
Production: In production by July of 1978.
Cost: $279.95.   (cont.)

80-103A (cont.)

This early S-100 internal modem was from Hayes who later standardized the command-set for modems.

Value: $50-$75

Digicom Data Products AC-312
Type: Acoustic-coupler modem.
Speed: 300 to 1200 bps.
Production: In production by August of 1978.
Cost: $245 for 300 bps unit, $495 for 1200 bps unit. A board for upgrading 300 bps to 1200 bps was $370.

This unit operated over dial telephone lines, and had "5 bps reverse channel capability."

Value: $15-$40

Omron Electronics Series 8300
Type: Acoustic-coupler modem.
Speed: 300 bps.
Interface: RS-232C serial or 20 mA current-loop.
Production: In production by August of 1978.
Cost: $275.

Value: $15-$40

Later version of
A 242A/36

Anderson Jacobson A 242A/36
Type: Acoustic-coupler modem, also having direct-connect capability.
Speed: As high as 450 bps.
Production: In production by May of 1979.
Cost: $265.

The May 1979 Byte said it "Is made specifically for Digital Equipment Corporation's LA 36 teleprinter terminal."

Value: $20-$50

Dynamic Devices
Type: Acoustic-coupler modem.
Speed: 300 bps.
Interface: RS-232C and 20 mA interfaces.
Production: In production by May of 1979.
Cost: $169.95.

This kit was developed for the personal-computer market, and claims asserted it could be "assembled in less than 15 minutes." It could operate in both originate and answer modes.

Value: $15-$40

Gandalf LDM 404B
Type: Limited-distance modem.
Speed: 4800 bps for distances up to 50 miles.
Physical: Available in desktop or rack-mounted styles.
Production: In production by May of 1979.

Value: $20-$50

Micromodem 100

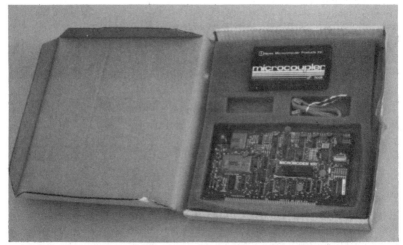

Micromodem 100 in original packaging with coupler showing

Micromodem 100 in original packaging with manual

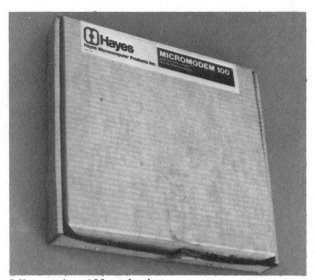

Micromodem 100 packaging

D.C. Hayes Associates Micromodem 100
Type: Autodial modem.
Speed: 100 and 300 bps.
Production: Introduced in 1979.
Cost: $399.

Value: $50-$75

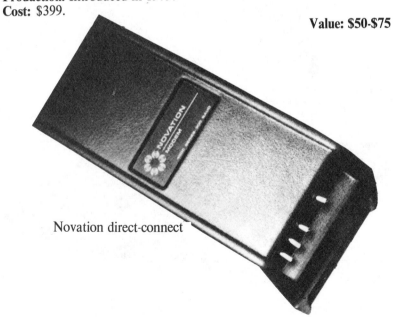

Novation direct-connect

Novation acoustic coupler

Hamilton/Avnet Novation 4000 Series
Type: Modem (acoustic or direct-connect).
Speed: 300 Baud.
Production: In production by September of 1979.

Value: $20-$50

Cat

Hamilton/Avnet Cat
Type: Acoustic-coupler modem.
Production: In production by September of 1979. (cont.)

Cat (cont.)
Cost: Less than $199.

Advertisements called this unit "a breakthrough for modems. Sleek, silent, compact, Cat is Novation's new acoustically coupled modem designed especially for the small computer user. Easy to use, simple to install, Cat is ideal for both small business and personal computer applications."

Value: $20-$50

103-LP

UDS (Universal Data Systems) 103-LP
Type: Direct-connect modem.
Speed: 0 to 300 Baud.
Production: In production by March of 1980.
Cost: "less than $200."

The 103-LP did not have an AC line cord. All power came from the telephone lines.

Value: $20-$40

OSI (Ohio Scientific Instruments) AC-11P
Type: Acoustic-coupler modem.
Speed: 300 Baud.
Interface: RS-232.
Production: In production by April of 1980.
Cost: $199.

Value: $20-$50

Smartmodem 300

Smartmodem 300 packaging, power transformer and manual

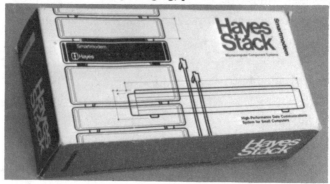

Smartmodem packaging

D.C. Hayes Associates Smartmodem 300
Production: Introduced in 1981.

This modem is significant in that it introduced the industry-standard Hayes command set.

Value: $50-$100

III-7. APPLICATIONS (SOFTWARE):

The earliest personal computers came with little or no software. Their owners were expected to program in the machine-language code of the microprocessor they were running. One of the earliest pieces of useful software available for personal computers was an interpreter for the BASIC language. This allowed less knowledgeable users to easily program their machines. Since the commands were similar for various versions of BASIC, it also allowed the knowledge and programs developed on one type of machine to be quickly adapted to BASIC running on another machine.

Nonetheless, BASIC still required a moderate knowledge of computers and programming to be a useful tool. The earliest "general purpose" programs, wordprocessing programs like Electric Pencil, EasyWriter and Word-Star, made the personal computer an easily accessible and very useful tool. The introduction of VisiCalc, the first spreadsheet, greatly advanced the usefulness of the personal computer to the non-programming public, especially the business world, and caused a greatly increased growth in the personal computer market.

As stressed in the introduction, boxes and original packaging are important to the historical and collectible value of an object. They are especially important in the case of software products. Software is very etheral in nature, being information rather than a physical object, and the "packaging" has more collector's value than the code itself. A copy of an early program may be interesting to play with, but from an historical or collector's standpoint, the media (tape, disks, etc.), manuals, and boxes, comprise the greater part of the collectible "item". While original packaging, manuals, and disks will enhance the value of hardware, the prices given in this guide do not assume its presence. In the case of software, however, all media and manuals are assumed to be present (although the media may not be entirely readable) for the stated values to apply.

MicroSoft BASIC
Type: Programming language.
Production: Introduced in 1975 for the Altair.

This software was offered on paper tape, and was the first BASIC for microcomputers. It was available both in 4 K and 8 K versions.

Value: $200-$300

Objective Design Encounter
Type: Game.
Production: Introduced in 1975.

This software was supplied on paper tape as an assembly language listing, and was one of the first microcomputer games.

Value: $100-$150

Electric Pencil
Type: Word processor.
Production: Introduced in December of 1976.

This was the first commercial microcomputer word processor.

Value: $25-$75

EasyWriter
Type: Word processor.

Value: $15-$40

MicroPro WordMaster
Type: Word processor.
Production: Introduced in 1978.

This early word processor evolved into the popular Word Star.

Value: $15-$40

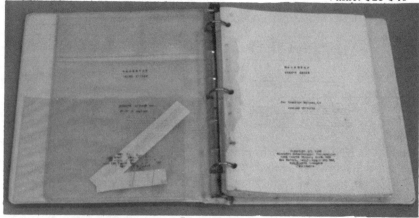

WordStar manual and disk holder. Original disks are missing.

WordStar manual

MicroPro WordStar
Production: Released in mid-1979.

Value: $20-$50

Inside of Apple II VisiCalc folder showing disks and manual

Apple II VisiCalc disks

External view of Apple II VisiCalc folder

(cont.)

310

Visi Calc (cont.)
Personal Software VisiCalc
Type: Spreadsheet.
Production: Released in 1979. VisiCalc sold 500 copies per month initially, but this rose as high as 12,000 copies per month in 1981. It was discontinued in 1985.
Cost: Initially $100, but it sold so well the price was raised to $150.

VisiCalc was the first spreadsheet and was very popular with businesses. It was first available on an Apple disk. It was a very important early application of the personal computer, and helped the sales of machines.
Value: $25-$75

Vulcan
Type: Database.
Production: Introduced in 1979.

This early database evolved into the popular dBASE II.
Value: $20-$50

Satellite Software International Word Perfect
Type: Wordprocessor.
Production: Introduced in 1980. In 1984 versions came out for the Tandy 2000, the DEC Rainbow, the Zenith Z-100, the Victor 9000 and the IBM PC.

Word Perfect was introduced for Data General Computers. Satellite Software later became Word Perfect Corporation.

Value: $20-$50, for versions issued by Satellite Software International.

III-8. MISCELLANEOUS:

One of the questions asked when personal computers were first introduced was "What can you do with them?" The early machines were basically toys for electronics hobbyists, and were seen as such. Eventually this question was answered with the development of applications like spreadsheets, wordprocessing programs, and databases. However, over the years there have been numerous other applications. Many of these involved hardware, and a few of the interesting ones are reviewed here in what is basically a catch-all for important items that do not fall in any other category.

Alpha Supply Velostat
Type: Conductive floor mat.
Physical: Two sizes were available: 24" by 32" and 4' by 8'. Came with a 15-foot ground cord, 1 Meg ohm resistor, and snap fasteners.
Production: In production by June of 1976.
Cost: Small: $28.80, large: $98.40.

This was a grounded floor mat to dissipate static charge to protect semiconductor equipment.

Value: $5-$10

MRS AM6800
Type: Motorola M6800 processor board for the Altair 8080.
Physical: S-100 card.
Production: In production by June of 1976.

Claims asserted this card would not interfere with the normal execution of the 8080.

Value: $20-$40

SSM after assembly, showing box and disk

Music Synthesizer kit box

SSM (Solid State Music) Music Synthesizer Board
Type: Music synthesizer board.
Physical: S-100 card with outputs for speakers.

This kit was early precursor to today's "multi-media" sound cards.

Value: $15-$40

CT-1

Computalker Consultants CT-1 Synthesizer
Type: Voice-synthesizer card.
Physical: S-100 card.
Production: In production by January of 1978.
Cost: $395 for the CT-1 Synthesizer, $35 for the CSR1 software system.

Value: $15-$40

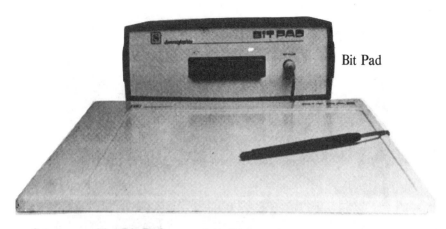

Bit Pad

Summagraphics Bit Pad
Type: Data-tablet digitizer.
Production: Introduced in 1978, and was available by July of 1978. An interface to the TRS-80 was introduced about July of 1979 for $175.

The Bit Pad was a digitizer using a stylus on a digitizing pad. It could also operate with a cross-hair cursor. It was one of the first digitizers for microcomputers.

Value: $25-$75

NewO Co. The Writehander
Type: Hemispherical typing keyboard.
Physical: A hemispherically-shaped base with keyboard keys mounted on it.
Production: Introduced about July of 1978.

This strange device could type all 128 ASCII characters and send the ASCII codes by number.

Value: $25-$75

TI (Texas Instruments) Speak and Spell
Type: Speech synthesizer.
Production: Introduced in 1978.

The Speak and Spell was described in the September 1990 BYTE as "the first talking toy to use digital speech synthesis."

Value: $20-$40

Terrapin   Terrapin Turtle
Type: Mobile robot.
Physical: This small hemispherical mobile robot was covered with a 3.5-inch radius dome, and was 5-inches high.
Production: Introduced about August of 1978.
Cost: $300 as a kit, $500 assembled.

This machine was mobile, and could sense contact through its dome. A speaker allowed it to emit sounds, and a pen-mount allowed it to draw. It could travel at about 6 feet per second.

Value: $50-$125

Research Computer Systems (IPS) Intelligent Power Strip
Type: TTL-Controlled AC Power Strip.
Production: Introduced about February of 1979.
Cost: $129.50.

This power strip could control motor speeds, dim and control lights, run appliances, etc. It was optically isolated from the computer, and came fully assembled.

Value: $10-$20

Mountain Hardware   Apple Clock
Type: Real-time clock card for the Apple II.
Physical: Full-length Apple II card.
Production: Introduced about May of 1979.
Cost: $199 assembled.

Advertisements claimed this was the first real-time clock for the Apple II. It had an on-board battery, and tracked the time and date in 1 ms increments, with an accuracy of +/-0.001%. It could be accessed from BASIC.

Value: $20-$40

Mountain Hardware A/D-D/A
Type: A/D and D/A converter card.
Physical: Full-length Apple II card.

Value: $20-$40

Sun-Flex Co. Glare Filter
Type: Glare Filter for CRT
Physical: This was an optical filter to cut CRT glare. It was made of microporous material.
Production: In production by June of 1979.

This early screen filter was available for TRS-80, PET, Sorcerer, SWTPC, and others.

Value: $5-$10

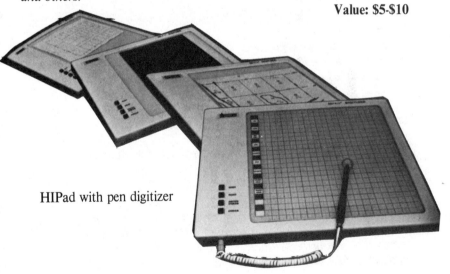

HIPad with pen digitizer

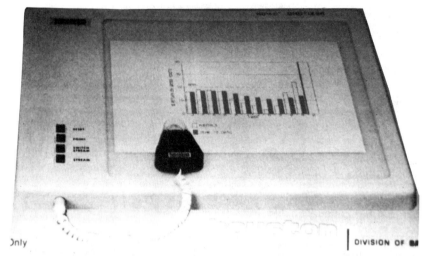

HIPad with mouse digitizer

Houston Instrument HIPad
Type: Digitizer.
Interface: Had both serial and parallel interfaces.
Production: In production by August of 1979.
Cost: $795.

This digitizer had a resolution of 0.005," +/-0.015", and an 11" by 11" digitizing surface. A liquid crystal display showing the X and Y coordinates was available as an option. It was a companion to the HIPlot.

Value: $25-$75

Tandy/Radio Shack Voice Synthesizer Module
Type: Voice Synthesizer.
Physical: An external module in the Radio Shack style. It had a silver-grey case with a black grille on the front.
Production: In production by October of 1979.
Cost: $25 to $50

Some of the suggested applications for this device were alarm systems, clocks, doorbells and use as a terminal for the blind. The speech was generated on phoneme synthesis (using 62 phonemes), and it reportedly could pronounce any word in the English language.

Value: $15-$40

SSM AIO Interface Card
Type: Serial and parallel interface card for the Apple II.
Physical: A card that plugs into the Apple II bus.
Production: In production by November of 1979.
Cost: $135 as a kit, $175 assembled.

Advertised as "the only board on the market that can interface the Apple to both serial and parallel devices. It can even do both at the same time."
Value: $20-$40

MicroSoft Soft Card
Type: Card running 8080 and Z-80 software.
Physical: Apple expansion card.
Production: Introduced in early 1980.

This card let the Apple run 8080 and Z-80 software.

Value: $75-$125

AST SixPakPlus
Type: Multiple function card.
Physical: PC bus card.
Production: Introduced in 1983.

This very successful card included serial, parallel, and game ports, a clock/calendar, and memory expansion. It came with utility software.
Value: $25-$50

Dayna Communications MacCharlie
Type: Macintosh-to-IBM adapter.
Physical: An enclosure with disk-drives that went next to the Macintosh CPU, and a jacket for the Macintosh keyboard containing function keys and a numeric keypad.
Production: Introduced in 1985.

This strange set of equipment adapted the Macintosh computer to run IBM software. When it was announced in BYTE magazine, many readers thought it was an April Fool's joke.
Value: $100-$200

APPENDIX A. MICROPROCESSORS

The development of the personal computer was made possible by the existence of the microprocessor. A microprocessor is a single-chip processor that can perform any of a group of operations, or instructions, on the values of entries in its registers or storage areas. In 1971 the first microprocessor, the Intel 4004, was introduced. It was intended initially as a programmable chip for use in the Busicom electronic desktop calculator. However, the capabilities of the 4004 and its immediate successors suited them for use in small computers, and several basic machines were produced using these processors. Spurred on by the promise of these early Intel devices, several other companies began to produce their own microprocessors. Today, the continued development of the microprocessor still drives the advancement of the personal computer.

Intel 4004
Word size: 4-bit.
Clock speeds: Could execute 60 K instructions per second.
Production: Introduced in 1971.
This was the first microprocessor. The name 4004 came from the number of transistors it replaced.

Intel 4040
This microprocessor was an intermediate between the 4004 and the 8008.

Intel 8008
Word size: 8-bit.
Cost: Prices ranged from around $80 on down to about $30.
Production: Introduced in 1972.
This successor to the 4004 was oriented more toward data and character manipulation. The 4004 was oriented toward arithmetic operation. This was the first microprocessor readily available to the hobbyist. It could address 16 K of memory.

Intel 8080
Word size: 8-bit.
Clock speeds: Could execute 290 K instructions per second.
Cost: Prices ranged from around $160 initially, down to less than $20 later on.
Production: Introduced in 1973.
Called "the first true general purpose microprocessor," this successor to the 8008 was very popular and became a standard for the personal computer industry. It could address 64 K of memory, and could run at a higher speed than the 8008.

Motorola 6800
Cost: $39.95.
Production: Introduced in 1975.

MOS Technology MCS6501
Production: In production by November of 1975.
This processor was pin-compatible with the Motorola 6800, but would not run 6800 software.

MOS Technology 6502
Word size: 8-bit.
Address bus: 16-bit.
Cost: About $25.
Production: Introduced in 1975.
Commodore bought MOS Technology.

National Semiconductor IMP-16
Word size: 16-bit.
Address bus: 16-bit.
Cost: About $160.
Production: In production by September of 1975.

National Semiconductor PACE
Word size: 16-bit
Production: In production by November of 1975.

Mostek Corp F-8
Word size: 8-bit.
Production: In production by January of 1976.

Intersil IM6100
Word size: 12-bit.
Production: In production by March of 1976.
This processor was software compatible with the PDP-8/E minicomputer.

TI TMS9900
Word size: 16-bit processor.
Address bus: 16-bit.
Clock speeds: 3 MHz.
Production: In production by April of 1976.

microNOVA mN601
Word size: 16-bit.
Production: In production by June of 1976.

Zilog Z-80
Word size: 16-bit.
Clock speeds: Up to 2 MHz.
Cost: $69.95.
Production: Introduced in 1976.
The Z-80 was compatible with the 8080, but had a more powerful instruction set.

Signetics 2650
Production: In production by August of 1976.

National Semiconductor SC/MP ("SCAMP")
Word size: 8-bit.
Address bus: 16-bit.
Cost: $99.
Production: Introduced about September of 1976.
The September 1976 BYTE stated the SC/MP was "designed to fill a gap between clumsy 4 bit microprocessors and the currently available 8 bit microprocessors."

Intel 8085
Cost: $250 for the processor and development kit.
Production: In production by July of 1977.
Called "the most advanced microcomputer" in the November 1977 BYTE.

Motorola 6809

DEC (Digital Equipment Corp.) LSI-11
Production: In production by September of 1977.

RCA 1802
Production: Introduced in 1976.

Intel 8088
Word size: 16-bit internal, 8-bit external.
Address bus: 20-bit.
Production: Introduced in 1979.
This processor was used in the IBM PC and its clones, and hence was very important.

Intel 8086
Word size: 16-bit internal and external.
The 8086 was the companion processor to the 8088.

Intel 80186
Word size: 16-bit.
The 80186 had more functions than 8088.

Toshiba T-3444
Production: In production before 1984.
The T3444 was the first Japanese microprocessor.

Intel 80286
Word size: 16-bit internal and external.
Address bus: 24-bit.
Production: Introduced in 1982.
The 80286 was the popular successor to the 8088.

NEC (Nippon Electric Co.) V20 and V30
Production: In production by 1985.

APPENDIX B. ACRONYMS AND TERMINOLOGY

As the technology of personal computers and calculators rapidly advanced, the nomenclature changed to keep up with it, leaving behind unused and forgotten terms as new ones were generated. This appendix is meant to supply sufficient terminology, old and new, to allow an understanding of the descriptions in this book.

A/D: Analog to Digital signal conversion.
ACR: Audio Cassette Recorder, used the store data.
ANSI: American National Standards Institute, an organization that develops standards for the electronics industry.
ASCII: American Standard Code for Information Interchange, a code for relating characters, alphanumeric and other, to 8-bit (265) numeric values.
assembler: A program to convert assembly-language code to machine language.
assembly language: A very low-level language specific to an individual type of microprocessor.
BASIC: Beginner's All purpose Symbolic Instruction Code, a very popular and simple high-level programming language.
Baud: The number of signal transitions in a data transfer sequence. It usually amounts to a transfer rate of one bit per second.
BBS: Bulletin-Board System, a computer and modem system into which users call. They are typically used for communication and ex-change of software.
bit: Binary digIT, it can take on the value 0 or 1.
BIOS: Basic Input/Output System, the boot ROM on IBM PCs and their derivatives.
bpi: Bits Per Inch, a measure of data density on paper or magnetic tapes.
bps: Bits Per Second, a measure of data transfer rate.
bubble memory: A form of nonvolatile magnetically-based solid-state memory.
byte: A series of bits, typically 8.
CAD: Computer Aided Design. Design assisted with the use of drafting and product-design software.
chad: A small disk or rectangle of paper produced when a hole is punched in a card or paper tape.
CMOS: Complementary Metal-Oxide Semiconductor, low-power RAM in which system configuration information is stored in some AT-class and newer IBM and clone machines.
COBOL: Common Business Oriented Language, a language aimed at record-keeping.
compiler: A program that converts high-level code to machine language.

cpi: Characters Per Inch, the density of characters on a printer or screen display.

cps: Characters Per Second, a measure of the transfer rate of information, as from a computer to printed hard copy. Sometimes denotes Cycles Per Second.

CPU: Central Processing Unit, the microprocessor chip, but sometimes the entire enclosure containing the processor board, power supply and disk drives is referred to as the CPU. See also MPU and microprocessor.

CRT: Cathode Ray Tube, the projection tube on whose surface the display of the computer can be projected. Often taken to mean the entire cathode-ray-tube monitor with housing and associated electronics.

D/A: Digital to Analog signal conversion.

DIP: Dual Inline Package, an IC with two rows of connector pins.

DMA: Direct Memory Access.

DOS: Disk Operating System, an operating system using disks as storage. Sometimes refers to MS-DOS or PC-DOS specifically.

dot matrix: A printing mechanism comprised of pins, usually 9 or 24, that strike and inked ribbon against the paper. Dot matrix printers are sometimes referred to as impact printers.

double-shot keys: Keyboard keys with their labels molded in, as opposed to printed or stuck on.

DRAM: Dynamic Random Access Memory. A form of RAM.

DS: Double sided, referring to writing on both sides of a magnetic disk.

EBCDIC: Extended Binary Coded Decimal Interchange Code, a code for relating characters to numeric values, similar to ASCII.

endec: ENcoder/DECocer, a device used to encode and decode the data going to and from the computer's expansion bus and the magnetic heads of a disk drive.

EPROM or EROM: Erasable (Programmable) Read Only Memory, a type of memory that can retain its contents when powered-down, and can be re-written after an erasing procedure.

ESDI: Enhanced Small Device Interface, a tape and disk-drive interface convention. It was established by Maxtor Corporation in 1983.

FDD: Floppy Disk Drive.

firmware: Software permanently stored in ROM.

fixed drive: A hard disk drive. Also known as an HDD or Winchester drive.

FM: Frequency Modulation. A protocol for writing data to disks.

FORTRAN: FORmula TRANslator, a language used mainly for computations. It was developed for use on mainframes.

GUI: Graphic User Interface, a computer interface based on visual cues and the manipulation of images, rather than on command lines and textural input.

HDD or HD: Hard Disk Drive. Also known as a fixed drive or Winchester drive.

hex: Hexadecimal, a base -16 number system, comprised in computers of 16 bits or two bytes.

HPIL: Hewlett-Packard Interface Loop. A protocol for communication between devices.

I/O: Input/Output devices on a computer to allow data to be sent out or in.

IC: Integrated Circuit, a small electronic device incorporating many components. The basic building-block of microcomputers.

IDE: Integrated Drive Electronics, a hard disk drive configuration in which the endec is located on the drive itself, as opposed to on the controller card.

impact printer: A printing mechanism that impacts a ribbon to print a character on the underlying paper. Dot matrix and daisywheel printers are both impact printers.

interpreter: A program to interpret and execute commands from a high-level language, like BASIC. Unlike a compiler, which converts the entire program before executing it, each command is interpreted and executed as it is encountered.

ISA: Industry Standard Architecture, a standard bus derived from the IBM PC bus.

K: Same as Kilo.

KHz: One thousand cycles per second.

Kilo: One thousand.

LAN: Local Area Network, a collection of two or more computers interconnected and able to communicate with each other.

LED: Light Emitting Diode, a diode which emits light when current is passed through it. Often these were arranged in patterns such that illuminating various sequences displayed alphanumeric characters. They were also used as single-light displays to depict the state of a single bit.

line printer: A printer that can print an entire line at a time.

LSI: Large Scale Integration, an IC incorporating a large and complex collection of electronic devices working in an integrated fashion to perform complex tasks. Refers to integration of components beyond that of a single microprocessor.

μ : Micro. one millionth.

m: Same as milli.

M: Same as Mega.

machine language: The actual binary code read and interpreted by the microprocessor. It is the lowest level at which a computer can be programmed.

magnetic tape: Strips of magnetically-sensitive tape, usually kept on rolls, on which data is stored.

mainframe: In early microcomputer terminology this referred to the passive backplane bus of the S-100, SS-50, and other early machines.

MCA: Micro Channel Architecture, a bus design used by IBM on some of their PS/2 machines.

Mega: One million.

MFM: Modified Frequency Modulation. A protocol for writing data to disks.

MHz: One million cycles per second.

micro: One millionth.

micro floppy: A 3.5-inch diameter floppy disk in a hard plastic case with a sliding metal window.

microcomputer: A computer based on a microprocessor.

microprocessor: The main chip of a microcomputer that executes the machine-language code, the microprocessor chip. See also CPU and MPU.

milli: One thousandth.

mini-floppy: 5.25-inch diameter floppy disk, so called because it was small compared to the 8-inch floppys previously in use.

MIPS: Million Instructions Per Second, a unit of measure of the rate at which a microprocessor can execute instructions.

modem: MOdulator/DEModulator, a device to translate digital signals to audio tones (and vice-versa) for transmission on telephone lines.

MPU: MicroProcessor Unit, the microprocessor chip. See also CPU and microprocessor.

MTBF: Mean Time Between Failure, a measure of expected longevity of a device in use.

ms: Millisecond, one thousandth of a second.

μ: Microsecond, one millionth of a second.

n: same as nano.

nano: One billionth.

non-impact: Used to refer to electrostatic or thermal printers.

ns: Nanosecond, one billionth of a second.

OEM: Original Equipment Manufacturer, a manufacturer of equipment who supplies it to another company who then sells it under its own name.

octal: Base 8 number system.

paper tape: Strips of paper onto which holes could be punched to encode binary data.

parallel port: An I/O port with several bits represented simultaneously on different wires.

peripheral: A device to work in concert with another, more critical machine (typically the computer).

pin-impact: A printing technology employing a matrix of pins which could impact a ribbon in selected patterns to imprint a character on the underlying paper. Also referred to as dot-matrix and impact printers.

POST: Power On Self Test, a sequence of tests some computers run from their ROM upon powering up.

PROM: Programmable Read Only Memory, a type of memory that can retain its contents when powered-down.

QWERTY: The conventional layout for characters on a keyboard, as derived from typewriter keyboards.

RAM: Random Access Memory, the fast electronic memory in which the computer stores its instructions, and sometimes the data it is processing.

RAM disk or drive: A portion of RAM allocated to store and retrieve data in the manner of a disk drive. The same as a silicon disk.

RLL: Run Length Limited. A protocol for writing data to disks.

ROM: Read Only Memory, a type of memory that can retain its contents when powered-down.

RPN: Reverse Polish Notation, a type of notation used on some calculators.

RS-232: Recommended Standard number 232. A serial data convention. Also RS-232C.

SASI: Shugart Associates Systems Interface, a system interface convention, related to the later SCSI.

serial I/O: A technique for sending data sequentially across a single pair of wires.

S-100: The first microcomputer bus standard, initiated by the Altair. Also known as the Altair bus.

SCSI: Small Computer Systems Interface, a system interface convention, related to the earlier SASI.

silicon disk: A portion of RAM allocated to store and retrieve data in the manner of a disk drive. The same as a RAM drive.

SRAM: Static Random Access Memory. A form of RAM.

SS: Single sided, referred to writing on one side of a magnetic disk.

SS-50: A bus standard on early personal computers, an alternate to the S-100 bus.

SIMM: Single Inline Memory Module, a form of memory packaging with the contacts in a line.

SIP: Single Incline Package, a form of memory packaging with pin contacts in a line.

ST-506/412 interface: A hard-drive controller interface based on the Seagate ST-506 and ST-412 hard drives. It became an industry standard.

Teletype: A terminal, produced by Teletype Corporation, whose input was a keyboard and whose output was a paper printout.

terminal: A device to allow a human to interact with a computer, typically using a CRT for display and a keyboard for input.

UART: Universal Asynchronous Receiver Transmitter, the device that prepares data for transmission or reception through a serial port.

TPI: Tracks Per Inch, a measure of data density on magnetic media.

Winchester drive: A hard disk drive, also known as a fixed drive or HDD.

word: A unit of memory. In microcomputers it was often 8 bits.

WORM: Write Once Read Many, a media that can be written to only once, but read many times.

APPENDIX C. CHRONOLOGY OF PERSONAL COMPUTER DEVELOPMENT.

1956:

The Geniac was in production by the fall of this year. Sold primarily as a toy, this type of machine was arguably the first electronic digital personal computer.

1963:

Bell Punch Company introduced what was likely the first commercial desktop electronic calculator. About the size of a cash register, and costing several hundred dollars, it was the precursor of the hand calculator.

1968:

Hewlett-Packard introduced the 9100A, an electronic desktop calculator that could perform scientific calculations and was instrumental in getting HP into the business of making computers.

1971:

The first microprocessor, the Intel 4004, was released.

The Busicom desktop electronic calculator, based on the new Intel 4004, was introduced. This was the first computing device to employ a microprocessor.

Hewlett-Packard introduced the 35, 45, and 80 pocket calculators.

1972:

Intel introduced the 8008, the first microprocessor readily available to the hobbyist.

1973:

Intel introduced the 8080. It became a standard for the personal computer industry.

CP/M was written.

The TV Typewriter appeared in Radio Electronics.

The 8008-based Scelbi 8H was introduced.

1974:

On January 17 Hewlett-Packard announced the 65 programmable scientific calculator.

The 8008-based Mark 8 was introduced in July.

Xerox produced the Alto. Although it was never sold commercially, some consider it the first personal computer.

1975:

The MITS Altair 8800 was announced in January and shipped in April. By the end of the year over 5000 had been sold.

The 8080-based Processor Technology SOL was introduced about April.

MicroSoft introduced its version of BASIC for the Altair. Offered on paper tape, it was written by Bill Gates and Paul Allen, and was the first BASIC for microcomputers.

Motorola introduced the 6800.

MOS Technology introduced the 6502.

On September 9 IBM announced the 5100. While perhaps too costly to be considered a personal computer as the term is defined here, it was IBM's first entry into the microcomputer market.

On September 16 Texas Instruments introduced the SR-52, an early and popular programmable scientific calculator.

MOS Technology introduced the single-board, 6502-based Kim-1.

1976:

The single-board, 6502-based Apple I began production in July. A total of about 200 were made.

Processor Technology released its VDM video board. It, and Cromemco's TV Dazzler, were the first graphics cards for machines using the S-100 bus introduced by the Altair.

About August STM Systems introduced the BABY! 1, likely the first personal computer to be sold specifically as a portable.

Zilog introduced the Z-80. It was compatible with the 8080, but had a more powerful instruction set.

About December Shugart introduced its 5.25-inch Minifloppy drive. Belt-driven by a DC motor, this was one of the first 5.25-inch floppy drives.

The first commercial microprocessor word processor, Electric Pencil, was introduced in December.

1977:

MITS was sold to Pertec on May 22.

The Heath H8 and H11 machines were introduced.

In April the Apple II was introduced. By the end of the year production was doubling every three to four months. Advertising was aimed at the home market.

The Commodore PET 2001 was introduced in June by Commodore Business Machines, a maker of hand-held calculators.

On August 3 Tandy announced the TRS-80 Model I. By September, 10,000 were sold.

1978:

Atari introduced the 400 and 800 machines, aimed at game applications.

Digital Group announced the Bytemaster, an early, well-integrated portable.

In June Apple introduced the Disk II, a 5.25-inch floppy disk drive, for $495. It came with disk operating system software that gave "dynamic disk space allocation" which allowed the operator to store or retrieve a file on the disk without having to know the size of the file or its storage location on the disk.

Epson introduced the MX-80, and expanded the market for low-cost printers. Shugart Associates announced its SA-4000 hard-disk drive about June. Available in 14.5 and 29 megabyte capacities, it was referred to as a "Winchester" drive, as were all hard drives at the time.

1979:

The Apple II + was introduced in June.

In mid-year MicroPro introduced Word Star.

Intel introduced the 8088, the microprocessor used in the IBM PC and its clones.

Personal Software introduced VisiCalc, the first spreadsheet. It sold 500 copies per month initially, but this rose as high as 12,000 copies per month in 1981.

1980:

The Sinclair Research ZX80 was initially marketed in the U.K., and tens of thousands of units were sold in Europe by the end of the year. Ultimately, this became the first microcomputer to sell for under $200.

Tandy introduced its TRS-80 Pocket Computer. The PC-1 was manufactured by Sharp, and was the first battery-powered computer sold in the U.S.

In June the HHC was introduced by both Panasonic and Quasar Data Products. This early palmtop was produced by Matsushita.

Seagate introduced its ST-506 5.25-inch hard-disk drive, with a capacity of 5 megabytes. The interface for this drive, along with that of the ST-406 which was introduced about a year later, set the ST-506/412 standard that became widely used in the industry.

Satellite Software International introduced Word Perfect.

Apple introduced the III in September. It was never as successful as hoped.

1981:

In April the first popular portable computer, the Osborne 1, was introduced. Sales rose to $100 million in less than two years, but on September 13, 1983, the company went bankrupt.

On August 12 IBM introduced the 5150 PC. Based on the 8088, it brought standardization to the personal computer market. Between August and September about 13,000 were sold.

PC-DOS version 1.0 was released along with the IBM PC in August.

Hayes introduced its Smartmodem 300 that established the industry-standard Hayes command set.

The Epson HX-20 was introduced. Containing a small printer, it is considered by many to be the first true laptop computer.

1982:

The Commodore 64 was introduced. It came with color graphics and sound capability.

Intel introduced the 80286, the popular successor to the 8088.

About September Iomega introduced its Bernoulli Box, and early removable hard drive.

In November the first Compaq portable was introduced, running version 1.1 of MS-DOS.

1983:

In January Apple introduced the Lisa, Apple's first GUI machine, and a precursor to the Macintosh.

On March 8 the IBM 5160 PC XT was introduced. This updated version of the original PC had 8 expansion slots, and the cassette port of the earlier machines was deleted.

Tandy introduced the TRS-80 Model 100. This early notebook had an integral modem.

1984:

In January Apple released the Macintosh 128. This was the first popular GUI machine, and it gave rise to the very successful line of Apple Macintosh machines. In September a 512 kilobyte version was introduced.

AT&T entered the personal computer market with the introduction on June 26 of the PC 6300.

The 80286-based IBM 5170 PC AT was introduced on August 14. It had the ability to address 16 megabytes of memory, and had 16-bit expansion slots.

1985:

Intel introduced the 80386DX.

Commodore introduced the Amiga 1000, complete with a GUI and multitasking.

1986:

In January the Toshiba T-1100 was introduced. While a relatively small number were sold, its successor, the T-1100 Plus, was extremely popular and helped launch the laptop market.

The Apple Macintosh Plus was introduced in January.

On April 2 IBM introduced its first laptop, the 5140 Convertible PC.

1987:

On April 2 IBM discontinued the 5150 PC.

IBM introduced the PS/2 Series.

Apple introduced the Mac II.

1988:

The NeXT was announced in San Francisco.

Intel announced the 80386SX.

In October NEC introduced the UltraLight. While a 2400-Baud modem was standard in this early notebook, it lacked the conventional disk-based storage found in later notebooks.

1989:

Apple introduced its first portable, the Mac Portable.

GRiD Systems announced the GRiDPad, a machine that could recognize handwriting made with its input pen.

Intel announced the 486DX.

Compaq introduced its LTE and LTE 286 notebooks in October. These were the first full-function notebook computers, including standard floppy and hard drives.

Late in the year Poquet introduced its Poquet PC. This handheld had a usable keyboard and had version 3.3 of MS-DOS in ROM. It could run 100 hours on AA batteries.

1991:

Around May Hewlett-Packard introduced its 95LX, a DOS-compatible palmtop with 512 kilobytes of RAM.

APPENDIX D. RECOMMENDATIONS TO THE BEGINNING COLLECTOR

Collecting anything is very personal. There are numerous reasons people collect things, and it is hard to single out a common motive. However, the central motive of many collectors will be a desire to assemble a set of machines spanning the development of the personal computer, and including the most important high points. Some collectors taken with this idea will have little detailed knowledge of the history of these machines. The following list has been compiled to give the beginning collector a first goal. The machines listed below are some of the more important and interesting pieces. Collectibility was also considered in compiling this list, and all the machines should be obtainable at reasonable cost and without excessive searching.

PERSONAL COMPUTERS:

Altair, SWTPC or IMSAI:
These machines introduced and popularized the concept of personal computers.

MOS Technology Kim-1, Synertek SYM-1, or Rockwell AIM-65
These early single-board personal computers were the first to employ the "mainboard" or "motherboard" design concept that is now found in all today's personal computers.

Apple II, Commodore PET 2001, or Tandy/Radio-Shack TRS-80 Model I:
These "appliance computers" legitimized personal computers and opened the market to a much wider segment of the population.

IBM 5150 PC:
The first IBM PC had a profound standardizing effect on the personal computer market. The standards it set still dominate the market today.

Apple MacIntosh 128 or 512:
Graphics User Interfaces are now heralded as the future of the personal computer. These were the first popular GUI machines.

Osborne 1:
This suitecase-sized luggable was the first popular portable microcomputer.

Compaq Portable:
This was the first Compaq computer, and the first DOS-based portable.

Compaq LTE or LTE 286:
With a 20 or 40 megabyte hard drive and a 1.44 megabyte 3.5-inch floppy drive, the LTE was the first full-function notebook computer.

Poquet PC:
The Poquet was a pioneer in the area of DOS-based hand-held computers.

Hewlett-Packard 95LX:
The 95LX was the first DOS-based palmtop, and a dramatic intersection of the trends of the decreasing size of personal computers and the increasing functionality of hand-calculators.

ACCESSORIES AND PERIPHERALS:

The following collection of accessories and peripherals gives a good overview of the development of these devices.

Data storage devices:

Paper tape reader

Early cassette recorder

8-inch floppy disk drive

5.25-inch floppy disk drive

ST-506/412-type 5.25-inch hard disk drive

Printers:

Adapted-typewriter

Thermal or electrosensitive

Daisywheel

Dot-matrix

Communications devices:

Hamilton/Avnet Cat or other acoustic-coupler modem.

Hayes Smartmodem 300

Software:

MicroPro WordStar

Personal Software VisiCalc

HAND CALCULATORS:

Hewlett-Packard 35 or 45

Texas Instruments SR-51 or SR-52

APPENDIX E. THE COMPUTER COLLECTOR'S REGISTER

The Computer Collector's Register is a catalog of computer collectors. Compilation of this register began several years ago, and it has been valuable in estimating the interest, demand, and prices for various machines listed in this catalog. The following registration form can be submitted by collectors wishing to have their interests recorded.

Perhaps in the future this register will serve to facilitate communication between collectors, and as a forum where collectors from all over can exchange information, want lists, etc. Responses to the register could be organized, and collectors with similar interests could be put in contact with each other.

APPENDIX F. REFERENCES

GENERAL PERSONAL COMPUTER HISTORY:

These references discuss the general history of the development of the personal computer:

Augarten, Stan, 1984, *Bit by Bit, an Illustrated History of Computers,* Ticknor and Fields, New York. Chapter Nine.

Freiberger, Paul, and Michael Swaine, *Fire in the Valley, The Making of the Personal Computer,* 1984, Osborne/McGraw-Hill, Berkeley, CA.

Goldberg, Adele, Ed., *A History or Personal Workstations,* 1988, ACM Press.

Layer, Harold A., 1989, "Microcomputer History and Prehistory — An Archaeological Beginning," *Annals of the History of Computing,* Vol. 11, No. 2, pp. 127-130.

HISTORY OF THE IBM PC:

While these references are basically technical discussions, they contain significant information on the development of the IBM PC:

Brenner, Robert C., *IBM Personal Computer Troubleshooting and Repair for the IBM PC, PC/XT and PC AT,* 1989, Howard W. Sams and Co., Carmel, Indiana.

Buchsbaum, Walter H., 1980, *Personal Computer Handbook,* Howard W. Sams and Co., Inc., Indianapolis.

Mueller, Scott, 1988, *Upgrading and Repairing PCs,* Que Corporation, Carmel, Indiana.

COMPUTER AND CALCULATOR
COLLECTOR'S REGISTER
Registration Form and Survey

Name _____

Address_____

Date_____

Are you a collector of old computers or calculators? _____

Are you a user of old computer or calculators?_____

Interests:

Equipment _____

Age_____

Equipment _____

Age_____

Equipment _____

Age_____

Equipment _____

Age_____

SEND TO:

COMPUTER AND CALCULATOR COLLECTOR'S REGISTER
Post Office Box 2626
Ann Arbor, Michigan   48106

APPENDIX G. ALPHABETICAL LISTING OF MACHINES

The organization of this catalog is chronological. The subjects of the main chapters appear approximately in chronological order, and the machines within each chapter are listed approximately in the order in which they were introduced into the market. In this way, the structure of the guide serves as an evolutionary history of the machines it covers. The following alphabetical listing is supplied in the interests of finding a particular machine quickly and easily. Each machine is listed twice, once by the name of the manufacturer and once by the model name, to allow searching by either.

Listing by Make

make	model	page
Apple	Lisa 2	176
Apple	Mac Portable	197
Apple	Macintosh 128	177
Apple	Macintosh 512	178
Apple	Macintosh Plus	178
Apple	ProFile	250
Apple	Silentype	261
Applied Computer Sys.	Robotype	257
AST	SixPakPlus	319
Astral	2000	47
AT&T	6300	165
AT&T	6310	174
AT&T	6300 Plus	169
AT&T	6312 WGS	175
AT&T	Unix PC	151
Atari	400	125
Atari	800	126
Atari	1200XL	145
Atari	520ST	151
Axiom	EX-800	258
Axiom	EX-801 MicroPrinter	262
Axiom	EX-820 MicroPlotter	286
Axtrix		189
Bally	Professional Arcade	80
Bowmar	MX90	6
Bowmar	MX100	6
Bowmar	MX140	6
Bowmar	TP-3120	258
BPI	MicroNOVA	75
Byte	8	71
C.Itoh Ele.	7040 and 7040-T	271
Calcomp Computer Prod.	140/142/142M	228
Cannon	CX-1	148
Casio	FX-9000P	139
Casio	Mini Printer	6
CDC Phoenix		246
Centi-Byte		291
Central Data	16 K RAM Board	294
Centronics	700	281
Centronics	701	282
Centronics	730	280
Centronics	779	280
Centronics	703 and 779 printers	276
Centronics	P1 and S1	260
Chrislin Industries	CI-103	131
CMC Marketing	MCS-PT112/32	64
CMR Computer Mfg. Co.		290
Coleco	Adam	145
Columbia Data Prod.	VP Computer	187
Columbia Data Prod.	MPC 1600-4	154
Commodore	64	141
Commodore	1400	5
Commodore	8000 Series	132
Commodore	Amiga 1000	178
Commodore	F4146R	11
Commodore	PET 1540 (1541)	240

340

make	model	page
Commodore	PET 2001	104
Commodore	PET 2021 Ser. Printer	264
Commodore	PET 2022 Ser. Printer	279
Commodore	PET 2023 Ser. Printer	278
Commodore	PET 2040 (2041) 239	
Commodore	PET C2N	221
Commodore	VIC-20	134
Comp-Sultants	Micro-440	32
Compaq	Compaq Plus	186
Compaq	Deskpro 386	174
Compaq	LTE	201
Compaq	LTE 286	202
Compaq	Portable	184
Comprint	912	263
Compucolor	8051	110
Compucolor	II	114
Compucolor	Model III	114
Computalker Cons.	CT-1 Synthesizer	313
Computer Aid	CC-8 Digital Data Rec.	219
Computer Power and Light	COMPAL-80	70
Comterm	Hyperion	185
Convergent Technologies	WorkSlate	200
Corona	Starfire	250
Corona Data Systems	Portable PC	187
Corvus		245
Cromemco	16KZ	291
Cromemco	64KZ	292
Cromemco	System Three	74
Cromemco	System Zero/D	139
Cromemco	TV Dazzler	288
Cromemco	Z-1	48
Cromemco	Z-2	52
Cromemco	Z-2D	95
Cromemco	Z-2H	95
Cybersystems	Microcyber 1000	49
D.C. Hayes Assoc.	80-103A	299
D.C. Hayes Assoc.	Micromodem 100	303
D.C. Hayes Assoc.	Smartmodem 300	307
Data Dek	DD-100	214
Data General	microNOVA	42
Data General	Model 10	163
Datamedia	Elite 3052A Video Term.	289
datec	30 and 32	298
Dayna Communications	MacCharlie	319
DEC (Digital Equip. Corp.)	DECmate II	141
DEC	LSI-11	35
DEC	LSI-11	322
DEC	Rainbow 100	146
DEC	Rainbow 100 +	146
Digicom Data Prod.	AC-312	300
Digigraphic Systems Corp.	Extra-70	166
Digital	The Digital Group	48
Digital Electronics Corp.	DE68	180
Digital Electronics Corp.	DE68DT	107
Digital Group	Bytemaster	181

make	model	page
GRiD Systems	Compass Computer	194
GRiD Systems	GRiDPad	207
H&K	Singer 7100 and 7102	254
H2 Digital	Adapt-A-Typer	253
HAL Communications	Eight thousand	51
HAL Communications	MCEM-8080	41
Hamilton/Avnet	Cat	304
Hamilton/Avnet	Novation 4000 Series	304
Heath Dat. Sys.	H10 paper tape reader and punch unit	211
Heath Dat. Sys.	H11	57
Heath Dat. Sys.	H14 and WH14	282
Heath Dat. Sys.	H27 and WH27	234
Heath Dat. Sys.	H8	58
Heath Dat. Sys.	H89 and WH89	124
Heath Dat. Sys.	H9 Terminal	289
Heath Dat. Sys.	WH17	234
Helios		221
Hitachi	MB6890	148
Hitachi	TDS-IB	89
Houston Instrument	HIPad	318
Houston Instrument	HIPlot	286
HP	1	16
HP	10	16
HP	21	5
HP	22	9
HP	25	8
HP	27	10
HP	35	1
HP	45	3
HP	46	3
HP	55	5
HP	65	4
HP	67	11
HP	70	5
HP	80	2
HP	81	6
HP	85	127
HP	86	144
HP	91	9
HP	92	15
HP	97	11
HP	110	194
HP	150	157
HP	226	151
HP	19C	16
HP	25C	10
HP	29C	15
HP	31E	16
HP	32E	17
HP	33C	17
HP	33E	16
HP	34C	17
HP	37E	17
HP	38C	18
HP	38E	17

345

make	model	page
NEC	PC-100	159
NEC	PC-6000	139
NEC	PC-8000	135
NEC	Portable	200
NEC	Spinwriter 5530-P	257
NEC	UltraLight	201
NEC	V20 and V30	323
NEECO (New Eng. Ele. Co.)	Minimax I and II	124
Neltronics R&D Ltd.	Explorer/85	88
NewO Co.	The Writehander	314
Non-Lin. Sys./Kaypro Corp.	10	189
Non-Lin. Sys./Kaypro Corp.	II	185
North Star	Advantage	99
North Star	Floppy Disk Sys.	224
North Star	Horizon	54
Northwest Microcomp. Sys.	85/P	109
Noval	760	107
Objective Design	Encounter	308
Oki Electric	BMC if800 Model 20	135
Oki Electric	BMC if800 Model 30	135
Oliver Audio Eng. (OAE)	OP-80A	210
Olson	8080 Microcomputer	71
Omni Systems		293
Omron Electronics	Series 8300	300
	Orange	121
Osborne	1	183
OSI (Ohio Sci. Inst.)	AC-5A	284
OSI	AC-7B	289
OSI	AC-9TP	283
OSI	AC-11P	305
OSI	AC-14	268
OSI	C-D74	242
OSI	C3-OEM	83
OSI	C8P DF	96
OSI	Challenger 400	26
OSI	Challenger C1P	99
OSI	Challenger C1P MF	100
OSI	Challenger C2-8P	81
OSI	Challenger C4P	92
OSI	Challenger C4P DF	100
OSI	Challenger C4P MF	93
OSI	Challenger C8P	94
OSI	Challenger C8P DF	100
OSI	Challenger IP	66
OSI	Challenger II	67
OSI	Challenger IIP	67
OSI	Challenger III	73
OSI	Model 500	68
Otrona	Attache'	185
Panasonic	CF-150B	203
Panasonic	JB 3000	168
Panasonic	RL-H1000 HHC	205
Panasonic	RQ-309DS	220
Panasonic	Senior Partner (RL-H7000)	188
Parasitic Eng.	Equinox 100	59

make	model	page
Rockwell	AIM-65	85
S.D. Sales Co.		290
Sanyo	MBC-1000	147
Sanyo	MBC-555	166
Satellite Software Int.	Word Perfect	311
Scelbi Computer Consulting	8B	24
Scelbi Computer Consulting	8H	20
Scientific Research	Firmware System	107
Seagate	ST-412	250
Seagate	ST-506	249
Seals Electronics	PUP-1	69
Seequa	Chameleon	186
Seequa	Chameleon Plus	191
Sharp	MZ-2000	148
Sharp	PC-1500	205
Sharp	PC-5000	205
Shugart Assoc.	SA-400	224
Shugart Assoc.	SA-1000	243
Shugart Assoc.	SA-4000	243
Shugart Assoc.	SA-4008	245
Signetics	2650	322
Silonics	Quietype	285
Sinclair	105	7
Sinclair	Scientific Programmable	12
Sinclair Research	QL	148
Sinclair Research	ZX80	132
Sinclair Research	ZX81	139
Smoke Signal Broadcasting	BFD-68	227
Smoke Signal Broadcasting	Chieftan	238
Solid State Sales	Universal 4 K Memory Board Kit	295
Southwest Dev. Co.	Bulk Mem. Microcomp Audio Cass. Int.	212
Sperry	Peronal Computer	167
Sphere	1	24
Sphere	2	25
Sphere	3	25
Sphere	4	25
Sphere	Micro-Sphere 200	37
Sphere	One-Card Computer	28
SSM	AIO Interface Card	319
SSM (Solid State Music)	Music Synthesizer Board	313
Stearns Computer Sys.	PC	168
STM	Pied Piper	190
STM Systems	BABY! 1	179
Summagraphics	Bit Pad	314
Sun-Flex Co.	Glare Filter	317
SWTPC (Southwest Tech. Prod. Corp.)	6800	30
SWTPC	6800/2	78
SWTPC	AC-30 Cassette Interface	215
SWTPC	CDS-1	249
SWTPC	DMAF1	233
SWTPC	FD-8 Disk Memory	224
SWTPC	MC-6809	88
SWTPC	MF-68 Dual Minifloppy	228
SWTPC	MP-68	32
SWTPC	PR-40 Alphanumeric Printer	271

Listing by Model

model	make	page
912	Comprint	263
1000	Timex/Sinclair	140
1250	TI	7
1260	TI	9
1270	TI	9
1400	Commodore	5
1500	TI	4
1600	Eagle	166
1600	TI	10
1650	TI	10
1680	TI	14
1750	TI	13
1802	RCA	322
1810	Xerox	206
2000	Astral	47
2290	Litronix	12
2550	TI	4
2650	AMT (Applied Microtech.)	45
2650	Signetics	322
4004	Intel	320
4040	Intel	320
4615	National Semiconductor	12
4640	National Semiconductor	12
5050	TI	7
5100	IBM	101
5110	IBM	111
5120	IBM	134
5140 Convertible PC	IBM	195
5150 PC (PC1 and PC2)	IBM	152
5160 PC XT	IBM	155
5162 PC XT (Model 286)	IBM	170
5170 PC AT	IBM	171
6300	AT&T	165
6310	AT&T	174
6800	Motorola	321
6800	MSI (Midwest Sci. Inst.)	55
6800	SWTPC (Southwest Tech. Prod. Corp.)	30
8008	Intel	320
8051	Compucolor	110
8080	IMSAI (IMS Assoc., Inc.)	34
8085	Intel	322
8088	Intel	322
8510	Terak	49
8813	PolyMorphic Systems	74
80186	Intel	323
80286	Intel	323
008A	RGS Electronics	28
100 Intelligent Printer	Trendcom	264
103-LP	UDS (Universal Data Sys.)	305
1100FD	Tandy/Radio Shack	203
1200XL	Atari	145
140/142/142M	Calcomp Computer Prod.	228
16 II	TI	7
16 K RAM Board	Central Data	294
16KZ	Cromemco	291
1790 DataChron	TI	16

model	make	page
19C	HP	16
2250-II	TI	5
2500 Datamath	TI	2
250B Digital Tape Transport	MFE	216
2550 II	TI	9
25C	HP	10
29C	HP	15
30 and 32	datec	298
30 and 32	ElCom	297
31E	HP	16
3270 AT	IBM	173
3270 PC	IBM	158
32E	HP	17
33C	HP	17
33E	HP	16
3400 Sub-System	Intronics	238
34C	HP	17
360/65 Micro Bond Trader	Monroe	11
370 AT	IBM	174
370 XT	IBM	158
37E	HP	17
38C	HP	18
38E	HP	17
4100 cass. rec.	Techtran	217
44RD Ele. Slide Rule	Rockwell	13
4860 PCjr.	IBM	159
500 Series (500 and 520)	Quay	97
520ST	Atari	151
6300 Plus	AT&T	169
6312 WGS	AT&T	175
64KZ	Cromemco	292
64RD Ele. Adv. Slide Rule	Rockwell	13
6502	MOS Technology	321
6800/2	SWTPC (Southwest Tech. Prod. Corp.)	78
6809	Motorola	322
700 Ser. Printers	Motorola Microsystems	277
703 and 779 printers	Centronics	276
7040 and 7040-T	C.Itoh Ele.	271
71B Computer	HP	206
75 Portable Computer	HP	206
8/16 Univ. Microcomp. Dev. Sys.	Microkit	54
80F1	Quay	237
80-103A	D.C. Hayes Assoc.	299
8000 Series	Commodore	132
8080 Microcomputer	Olson	71
8080	Intel	320
8086	Intel	322
80AI	Quay	86
815 Datacassette	Techtran	219
820-II	Xerox	145
85/P	Northwest Microcomp. Sys.	109
86B	HP	150
87XM	HP	145
88T	MPI (Micro Peripherals, Inc.)	283
8B	Scelbi Computer Consulting	24

model	make	page
BASIC	MicroSoft	308
BASIC-8	Mikra-D	40
Bernoulli Box, Alpha-10	Iomega	251
Bernoulli Box, Beta-5	Iomega	251
beta-1	MECA	220
Betasystem	ibs (ind. business sys.)	87
BFD-68	Smoke Signal Broadcasting	227
Bit Pad	Summagraphics	314
BMC if800 Model 20	Oki Electric	135
BMC if800 30	Oki Electric	135
Bubcom	Systems Formulate Corporation	150
Bulk Mem. Microcomp Audio Cass. Int.	Southwest Dev. Co.	212
Business Analyst	TI	10
Bytemaster	Digital Group	181
C-D74	OSI (Ohio Sci. Inst.)	242
C2100	Jonos	189
C3-OEM	OSI (Ohio Sci. Inst.)	83
C8P DF	OSI	96
Cassette Deck	Viatron	218
Cat	Hamilton/Avnet	304
CC-40	TI	206
CC-8 Digital Data Rec.	Computer Aid	219
	CDC Phoenix	246
CDS-1	SWTPC (Southwest Tech. Prod. Corp.)	249
	Centi-Byte	291
Centronics 779	ibs (ind. business sys.)	278
CF-150B	Panasonic	203
Challenger 400	OSI (Ohio Scientific Inst.)	26
Challenger C1P	OSI	99
Challenger C1P MF	OSI	100
Challenger C2-8P	OSI	81
Challenger C4P	OSI	92
Challenger C4P DF	OSI	100
Challenger C4P MF	OSI	93
Challenger C8P	OSI	94
Challenger C8P DF	OSI	100
Challenger IP	OSI	66
Challenger II	OSI	67
Challenger IIP	OSI	67
Challenger III	OSI	73
Chameleon	Seequa	186
Chameleon	Seequa	191
Cheap Talk	Phone 1	298
Chieftan	Smoke Signal Broadcasting	238
CI-103	Chrislin Industries	131
CIS-30 +	PerCom Data Company	217
	CMR Computer Mfg. Co.	290
COMPAL-80	Computer Power and Light	70
Compaq Plus	Compaq	186
Compass Computer	GRiD Systems	194
Compucolor 8001	ISC (Intelligent Sys. Corp.)	105
Compcucorder 100	Sykes	217
Computer Aid 3M1	National Multiplex	213
Computer Aid 3M3	National Multiplex	214

357

model	make	page
EX-820 MicroPlotter	Axiom	286
EXORprint Printer	Motorola Semi. Con.	277
Explorer/85	Netronics R&D Ltd.	88
Extra-70	Digigraphic Systems Corp.	166
F-8	Mostek Corp.	321
F-8	Veras	45
F4146R	Commodore	11
F800	Microdata Systems	75
Familiarizor	EBKA Industries	39
FD-8 Disk Memory	SWTPC (Southwest Tech. Prod. Corp.)	224
FD-8 System	MSI (Midwest Sci. Inst.)	223
FDS-2	Synetic Designs Co.	227
Firmware System	Scientific Research	107
Flexible Disk Series B51	MPI (Micro Peripherals, Inc.)	229
Floppy Disk Sys.	North Star	224
Floppy Drive Kit	Sykes Datatronics	221
Fly Teleterm Reader 30	Teleterminal	209
FOS100	Extensys	232
Frugal Floppy	iCOM Microperipherals	222
FX-100 +	Epson	285
FX-9000P	Casio	139
Gavilan		194
Geniac		19
Glare Filter	Sun-Flex Co.	317
GNAT-PAC System 8	Gnat Computers	69
	GRI	193
GRiDPad	GRiD Systems	207
H8	Heath Dat. Sys.	58
H9 Terminal	Heath Dat. Sys.	289
H10 paper tape reader and punch unit	Heath Dat. Sys.	211
H11	Heath Dat. Sys.	57
H14 and WH14	Heath Dat. Sys.	282
H27 and WH27	Heath Dat. Sys.	234
H89 and WH89	Heath Dat. Sys.	124
	Helios	221
HHC	Quasar Data Prod.	205
HIPad	Houston Instrument	318
HIPlot	Houston Instrument	286
Horizon	North Star	54
HX-20	Epson	198
Hyperdrive	General Computer	251
Hyperion	Comterm	185
I	Apple	42
II	Apple	103
II	Compucolor	114
II	Eagle	141
II	Non-Lin. Sys./Kaypro Corp.	185
II +	Apple	122
IIc	Apple	149
IIc Plus	Apple	151
IIe	Apple	143
IIGS	Apple	151
III	Apple	133
iCOM Microfloppy	iCOM Microperipherals	226
IM6100	Intersil	41

model	make	page
MCS-PT112/32	CMC Marketing	64
MCS6501	MOS Technology	321
MD-690a	MicroDaSys	89
MD3	Morrow Designs	190
Megabyte Micro	IMSAI (IMS Assoc., Inc.)	55
Memorite	Vector Graphic	72
memory card	Processor Tech. Corp.	290
Mesa Two	A.O. Smith	108
MetaFloppy :1054	Micropolis	231
MF-68 Dual Minifloppy	SWTPC (Southwest Tech. Prod. Corp.)	228
Micro Decision	Morrow Designs	147
Micro M16	Mecromega	75
Micro-2	Digital Systems	77
Micro-440	Comp-Sultants	32
Micro-Altair	PolyMorphic Systems	39
Micro-Info. Sys.	Quasar Data Prod.	181
Micro-Sphere 200	Sphere	37
Micro68	EPA (Elect. Prod. Assoc.)	37
Micro68b	EPA	70
MicroAce		138
Microcyber 1000	Cybersystems	49
	MicroDaSys	116
MicroMind I	ECD	50
MicroMind II	ECD	51
Micromodem 100	D.C. Hayes Assoc.	303
MicroNOVA	BPI	75
microNOVA	Data General	42
	Micropolis hard drive	250
Mike 203A (Mike 2)	Martin Research	29
Mike 303A (Mike 3)	Martin Research	29
Mike 8	Martin Research	86
Mini 12	TLF	62
Mini Printer	Casio	6
Minimax I and II	NEECO (New Eng. Ele. Co.)	124
MinisPort	Zenith Data Sys.	201
	Mitsubishi	165
MMD-1	E and L Instruments	70
mN601	microNOVA	321
Model 10	Data General	163
Model 11/B	Andromeda Systems	70
Model 4000	Teleram	199
Model 500	OSI (Ohio Sce. Inst.)	68
Model 5000	Teleram	200
Model 990/4	TI	103
Model III	Compucolor	114
Money Manager	TI	13
	Mountain Computer	251
MP-40	MPI (Micro Peripherals, Inc.)	272
MP-68	SWTPC (Southwest Tech. Prod. Corp.)	32
MPC 1600-4	Columbia Data Prod.	154
MT-80P	Microtek	279
MTS-8	Mikra-D	40
Music Synthesizer Board	SSM (Solid State Music)	313
MX-80	Epson	277
MX90	Bowmar	6

361

model	make	page
Poly 88 System 16	PolyMorphic Systems	50
Poly 88 System 6	PolyMorphic Systems	51
	PolyMorphic Systems Video Term.	289
Portable	Compaq	184
Portable	NEC (Nippon Ele. Co.)	200
Portable PC	Corona Data Systems	187
Portable PC	IBM	188
Portable PC	Wordplex	186
PR-40 Alphanumeric Printer	SWTPC (Southwest Tech. Prod. Corp.)	271
PR-DW1	Algorithmics	266
Pragmatix 100	Electrolabs	130
PRD11	RDA	180
	Prime Radix Computer Synthesis	293
Prodigy	Prodigy Systems	128
Professional Arcade	Bally	80
Professional Computer	TI	154
Professional Computer (PC)	Wang Laboratories	154
ProFile	Apple	250
	Proko	210
PS-40	Telpar	259
PS-48E	Telpar	263
PS-80	Pers. Sys. Cons.	117
PUP-1	Seals Electronics	69
Pussycat 650 CRT Page Printer	Perkin-Elmer	260
QDP-100	Quasar Data Prod.	98
QDP-300F1H10	Quasar Data Prod.	100
QDP-8100	Quasar Data Prod.	99
QL	Sinclair Research	148
Quietype	Silonics	285
Rainbow 100	DEC (Digital Equip. Corp.)	146
Rainbow 100 +	DEC (Digital Equip. Corp.)	146
RAM-68	MSI (Midwest Sci. Inst.)	294
Recomp-I	Reston	115
RL-H1000 HHC	Panasonic	205
RoadRunner	Micro-Office Sys. Tech.	200
Robotype	Applied Computer Sys.	257
Rodent	Kit House	57
RQ-309DS	Panasonic	220
S-100 Mainframe	Integrand	80
SA-400	Shugart Assoc.	224
SA-1000	Shugart Assoc.	243
SA-4000	Shugart Assoc.	243
SA-4008	Shugart Assoc.	245
SBC/9	Percom Data Company	97
SC-655	Melcor	11
SC/MP (SCAMP)	National Semiconductor	322
SC40	Kingsport	7
Scientific Programmable	Sinclair	12
	S.D. Sales Co.	290
Selectra-Term	MCD (Micro Comp. Dev.)	254
Senior Partner (RL-H7000)	Panasonic	188
Series 16	Pronto	167
Series 8300	Omron Electronics	300
Silentype	Apple	261
Singer 7100 and 7102	H&K	254

model	make	page
TMS9900	TI	321
TP-3120	Bowmar	258
TPC1	TeleVideo	190
	Tri-Tec modem	296
Triple I Phi-Deck Super Deck	Economy Co.	217
TRS-80 Color Computer	Tandy/Radio Shack	138
TRS-80 Computer Cassette Rec.	Tandy/Radio Shack	216
TRS-80 CR-510	Tandy/Radio Shack	212
TRS-80 Daisy Wheel Printer	Tandy/Radio Shack	268
TRS-80 Level-II	Tandy/Radio Shack	117
TRS-80 Line Printer II	Tandy/Radio Shack	281
TRS-80 Model 12	Tandy/Radio Shack	140
TRS-80 Model 16	Tandy/Radio Shack	144
TRS-80 Model 16B	Tandy/Radio Shack	144
TRS-80 Model 100	Tandy/Radio Shack	199
TRS-80 Model 200	Tandy/Radio Shack	195
TRS-80 Model 2000	Tandy/Radio Shack	159
TRS-80 Model 4	Tandy/Radio Shack	149
TRS-80 Model 4P	Tandy/Radio Shack	186
TRS-80 Model I	Tandy/Radio Shack	106
TRS-80 Model II	Tandy/Radio Shack	119
TRS-80 Model III	Tandy/Radio Shack	137
TRS-80 Pocket Computer	Tandy/Radio Shack	204
Turtle	Terrapin	315
TV Dazzler	Cromemco	288
TX-80	Epson	284
UC2000	Infinite	111
UltraLight	NEC (Nippon Ele. Co.)	201
Universal 4 K Memory Board Kit	Solid State Sales	295
Unix PC	AT&T	151
USR-310, 320, and 330	U.S. Robotics	299
V20 and V30	NEC (Nippon Ele. Co.)	323
V80	Vista Computer	230
V200	Vista Computer	237
V1000	Vista Computer	237
VDM	Processor Tech. Corp.	288
VDP-40	IMSAI (IMS Assoc., Inc.)	113
VDP-80	IMSAI (IMS Assoc., Inc.)	64
VDP-80/1000	IMSAI (IMS Assoc., Inc.)	61
Vector 1	Vector Graphic	49
Vector 1 +	Vector Graphic	50
Velostat	Alpha Supply	312
VIC-20	Commodore	134
VideoBrain	Umtech	125
VisiCalc	Personal Software	311
Voice Synthesizer Module	Tandy/Radio Shack	318
VP Computer	Columbia Data Prod.	187
VT1920	Mikra-D	39
Vulcan		311
WH17	Heath Dat. Sys.	234
Word Perfect	Satellite Software Int.	311
WordMaster	MicroPro	308
WordStar	MicroPro	309
WorkSlate	Convergent Technologies	200
WY-1000	Wyse	168

NOTES

NOTES

NOTES

NOTES

NOTES